P9-CDM-208

WITHDRAWN

Loewe, F   782.81
                                L82L
The Lerner and Loewe   c.1
  song book

Do not weed

Indexed in

Song Finder

Popular Song Index

ADULT DEPARTMENT

1. Fine Schedule
     1- 5 days overdue _____ grace period, no fine
     6-10 days overdue _____ 25¢ per item
     11-19 days overdue _____ 75¢ per item
     20th day overdue _____ $2.00 per item
2. Injury to books beyond reasonable wear and all
   losses shall be paid for.
3. Each borrower is held responsible for all books
   drawn on his card and for all fines accruing on
   the same.

FOND DU LAC PUBLIC LIBRARY
FOND DU LAC, WISCONSIN

PRINTED IN U.S.A.   Cat. No. 23 263

PHOTOGRAPHS BY KARSH

ALAN JAY LERNER   FREDERICK LOEWE

The
LERNER & LOEWE
Song Book

BY

Alan Jay Lerner and Frederick Loewe

MUSIC EDITED BY DR. ALBERT SIRMAY

COMMENTARY BY SCOTT SULLIVAN

SIMON AND SCHUSTER · NEW YORK · 1962

(Inventory 1977)

RUNNING COMMENTARY COPYRIGHT © 1962 BY ALAN J. LERNER AND FREDERICK LOEWE.

THIS BOOK IS AUTHORIZED FOR SALE IN THE UNITED STATES AND CANADA ONLY.

Permission for the use of the songs contained in this book has been granted by the respective copyright owners, Chappell & Co., Inc., Sam Fox Publishing Company, Inc., and Mara-Lane Music Corporation.

The songs in this book have all been protected by international copyright with all rights reserved, including the right of public performance for profit.

Any arrangement or adaptation of any of these compositions without the consent of the owners is an infringement of copyright.

PUBLISHED BY SIMON AND SCHUSTER, INC.,
ROCKEFELLER CENTER, 630 FIFTH AVENUE,
NEW YORK 20, N. Y.

THIRD PRINTING

LIBRARY OF CONGRESS CATALOG CARD NUMBER: 62-17983
MANUFACTURED IN THE UNITED STATES OF AMERICA
MUSIC TYPOGRAPHY BY MUSIC TYPE SERVICE, NASHVILLE, TENNESSEE
PRINTED BY MAHONY & ROESE, INC., NEW YORK, NEW YORK
BOUND BY H. WOLFF, NEW YORK, NEW YORK

782.81
L82L
c.1

CONTENTS

Paint Your Wagon, 81

PLAYBILL, BACKGROUND AND STORY, 82

My Fair Lady, 117

PLAYBILL, BACKGROUND AND STORY, 118

Gigi, 165

PLAYBILL, BACKGROUND AND STORY, 166

Camelot, 207

PLAYBILL, BACKGROUND AND STORY, 208

Index of Song and Show Titles, 255

The Day Before Spring

OPENED NOVEMBER 12, 1945, AT THE NATIONAL THEATRE—165 PERFORMANCES

Book and Lyrics by ALAN JAY LERNER ✥ *Music by* FREDERICK LOEWE

PRODUCED BY JOHN C. WILSON

ORCHESTRATION BY HAROLD BYRNS

SETS BY ROBERT DAVISON

BOOK DIRECTED BY EDWARD PADULA

VOCAL ARRANGEMENTS BY MR. LOEWE

COSTUMES BY MILES WHITE

BALLETS AND MUSICAL ENSEMBLES BY ANTONY TUDOR

PRODUCTION STAGED BY MR. WILSON

MUSICAL DIRECTOR: MAURICE ABRAVANEL

ORIGINAL CAST

[IN ORDER OF APPEARANCE]

KATHERINE TOWNSEND	IRENE MANNING
PETER TOWNSEND	JOHN ARCHER
BILL TOMPKINS	BERT FREED
MAY TOMPKINS	LUCILLE BENSON
ALEX MAITLAND	BILL JOHNSON
MARIE	KAROL LORAINE
LUCILLE	BETTE ANDERSON
LEONORE	LUCILLE FLOETMAN
MARJORIE	ESTELLE LORING
SUSAN	ARLOUINE GOODJOHN
ANNE	BETTY JEAN SMYTHE
GERALD BARKER	TOM HELMORE
JOE McDONALD	DON MAYO
HARRY SCOTT	ROBERT FIELD
EDDIE WARREN	DWIGHT MARFIELD
CHRISTOPHER RANDOLPH	PATRICIA MARSHALL
KATHERINE (in the book)	MARY ELLEN MOYLAN
ALEX (in the book)	HUGH LAING
VOLTAIRE	PAUL BEST
PLATO	RALPH GLOVER
FREUD	HERMANN LEOPOLDI

The Day Before Spring

THE FIRST MEETING BETWEEN ALAN JAY LERNER and Frederick Loewe took place in the Lambs Club in New York in 1942. It went this way:

Loewe: "I understand you write lyrics."

Lerner: "Yes."

Loewe: "Do you think you can write a musical with me in two weeks?"

Lerner allowed that he might be able to, and the two of them set off for Detroit, where they ground out, in the required time, a musical comedy entitled *The Life of the Party*. It flopped, but Lerner and Loewe soon returned to New York to cooperate on their first effort for Broadway.

Lerner was twenty-five, Loewe forty-two. They had come together from widely different backgrounds, and with dissimilar tastes and interests, to form what became indisputably one of the most brilliant words-and-music teams of a generation.

Lerner was the scion of a wealthy family: his father was the founder of the prosperous Lerner Shops. Before meeting Loewe, he had been educated at Choate and Harvard, where he had written two shows for the Hasty Pudding Club. In the two years after he was graduated he had worked as a radio scriptwriter, turning out more than five hundred shows. He had also hung on to his ambitions to write for the musical theater and had written several songs for a Lambs Club show, *The Gambols*.

These amateur efforts were what attracted Loewe, who had already composed the scores for two musicals, one for Broadway and another for the St. Louis Munic-

ipal Opera. Born in Berlin, the son of a famous Viennese actor, Loewe had begun his career as a concert pianist, making his debut with the Berlin Symphony Orchestra at the age of thirteen. He had studied music at Stern's Conservatory in Berlin, had won the coveted Hollander medal in 1922, and then had continued his studies with Ferruccio Busoni. He had come to America in 1924, and settled down to full-time composing. When Loewe approached Lerner, he had been signed by a California producer to write the opening show for a newly formed stock company in Detroit and he was temporarily without a lyricist. Hence the *ad hoc* partnership.

The first Lerner-Loewe offering to reach New York was a short-lived and not much regretted little musical called *What's Up?* Despite the show's lack of commercial success, the two men decided to continue their partnership. It was a sound decision, because it formed a first essential step in the development of a collaborative technique that would, in the end, contribute to a revolution in the American musical theater.

If one theme in the story of Lerner's and Loewe's remarkable artistic evolution overshadows all the others, it is that of the increasingly sophisticated integration of story with music, an integration that achieved its highest form in *My Fair Lady* in 1956. Indeed, some manifestations of that integration were already present in the authors' first moderately successful production, *The Day Before Spring*, which opened at the National Theatre in New York in the autumn of 1945 and ran till the spring of the following year.

No one, the librettist himself has since remarked, could claim that the book of that show was a classic of dramatic construction. There clung to it something of the aura of the alumni hijinks it set out to satirize. Still, there was much in it that was fresh and original. In an interview fifteen years after it opened, Lerner confessed to a growing nostalgia for the days before immense celebrity and increasing scruples had reined in his verbal flamboyance. There is a sense of hilarious freedom in *The Day Before Spring*, even in the sections that are the least dramatically defensible.

Among the show's distinguished achievements are several songs which conform closely to the Lerner-Loewe dictum that character ought to be the motivation for every melody and lyric in a musical play. "God's Green World," the pseudophilosophic homily delivered by the romantic novelist Alex Maitland, is a striking example of this.

The organic use of musical effects unaccompanied by sung lyrics, which is of great importance in *Brigadoon* and *Gigi*, was already present in the last scene of the first act of *The Day Before Spring*. The early show also has echoes of the hero's last-act internal monologue that is present in every other show that Lerner and Loewe have written. And the song "My Love Is a Married Man," though highly comic, deals with the sort of serious problem that the authors were to come increasingly to feel deserved a place in musical "comedy."

The Day Before Spring, produced and directed by John C. Wilson, was largely financed by Metro-Goldwyn-Mayer, which eventually bought the film rights for $250,000. Critical reception of the show was warm on the whole, if not wildly enthusiastic. Walter Winchell called the musical "a delight." Burton Rascoe hailed it as a "brilliant new addition to American operettas." It settled in for a comfortable run, and within weeks of the opening Lerner and Loewe were at work on a new play for the following year—*Brigadoon*.

I ⎡ THE OPENING SCENE of *The Day Before Spring* Katherine Townsend, a pretty, fashionable woman of thirty, is found reading in the living room of her New York apartment. She drops her book abstractedly to sing the show's title song: "Spring came the day I found you, and I forgot the day before spring…" (see p. 16).

Her husband Peter enters. He is as handsome as his wife is pretty, but there is a distinct contrast between his brisk, decisive manner and her dreamy, slightly discontented mood. It develops that he is on the point of leaving for the tenth reunion of his class at Harrison University. Though Katherine is a member of the same class—and, indeed, met and fell in love with Peter at the University—she has so far refused to accompany him to the reunion.

As Peter makes his last attempt to persuade her, their friends Bill and May—two other members of the reunion class, who also met and became engaged at Harrison—arrive to pick Peter up. All three of them offer Katherine a final invitation to come along, this time musically, but she remains adamant.

While the women are alone together briefly, May has a chance to tell Katherine that another of their old classmates, Alex Maitland, is scheduled to address the reunion crowd. Katherine is obviously affected by this news, though she refuses more vigorously than ever to go along.

As May and Katherine talk, it is revealed that Alex is the author of the book Katherine was reading at the opening curtain—*The Day Before Spring*—and that he and Katherine had been engaged at college, before Peter had come into the picture. One night they had decided to elope to a mountain honeymoon lodge at two in the morning. The project had failed when their car had broken down on the way, and Peter, who had happened quite by chance to be driving by the spot where they were stranded, had rescued them. After that incident, Katherine's romance with Alex had cooled, she had switched her affections to Peter and had finally married him, and Alex had been subsequently forgotten.

Alex's recently published book begins with an entirely undisguised account of his elopement with Katherine—except that in the fictional version the car does not break down. The couple reaches the lodge, gets married, and goes on to live the gay, romantic life they had dreamed of. Reading the book, Katherine has been deeply moved, and disturbed, by the contrast between her own apparently humdrum existence and the gloriously seductive picture painted by Alex.

After telling May all this, Katherine at last relents: she agrees to go to the reunion.

Alex arrives at Harrison ahead of the Townsends, and he is surrounded by a crowd of co-ed autograph seekers, who are peppering him with questions about literature, life, and love. He responds with his theory that all experience is valuable, that "the dream you dreamed ever of" lies waiting to be realized out in "God's Green World" (see p. 19).

During the Boston tryout, before the opening in New York, Al Hirschfeld made this sketch of a dream sequence with Irene Manning (Katherine), surrounded by Tom Helmore (Gerald), Patricia Marshall (Christopher), Bill Johnson (Alex), John Archer (Peter), Ralph Glover (Plato), Hermann Leopoldi (Freud), Paul Best (Voltaire), and Mary Ellen Moylan (Katherine in the book).

When the girls go off, Alex is joined by his man Friday, Gerald Barker, who informs him, rather offhandedly, that he saw the Peter Townsends registering at the local hotel a few minutes before. The information has a powerful effect on Alex, but before he can do anything about it he is engulfed in a crowd of yawping, howling Harrison graduates.

Following just after the reunion crowd is Christopher Randolph, the twenty-one-year-old, pretty, and aggressive daughter of the dean of Harrison. Her mission for the weekend is to find Peter, who was once a beau of her elder sister's and with whom she has been in love, at long distance and without ever meeting, for ten years. Though Alex is entirely uninterested in her or her problems, Gerald falls immediately, irretrievably in love with her.

Finally Katherine arrives. From the moment she and Alex meet, their old attraction for one another is rekindled. After a spell of standing and gazing at one another, each assuring the other that he hasn't "changed at all," they make a date to spend the afternoon walking together in the country, just as they used to do ten years ago.

Though they have still not returned from the walk by six that evening, Peter is entirely unconcerned. As he is out walking by himself, he is suddenly confronted by Christopher, who proclaims that she is in love with him. He is inclined to treat her announcement as a joke, but she soon proves that she is in dead earnest, and he flees. Left alone, Christopher sings a lament for her unhappy state, "My Love Is a Married Man" (see p. 23)—and, alas, the sort who is true to his wife.

It is eleven o'clock by the time Alex and Katherine finally get back to the University. They have had an enchanting afternoon, and the old magic has once again reasserted itself. As Alex evokes the mood of *The Day Before Spring*, Katherine admits that she is in love with him again.

In a fit of nostalgia, Alex suggests that they carry out the plan to elope that had failed ten years earlier—that they leave Harrison by car at two in the morning, so that they will arrive at the mountain lodge just as dawn is breaking and will spend their first night together in the mists of morning. From there, he assures her, they will go on to re-create in real life the fantasy he has constructed in his book, detail for detail.

Katherine is greatly tempted, but she still feels scruples about Peter. She goes off to find him, expecting—and half hoping—that he will be furiously jealous over her absence that afternoon. But she finds him entirely indifferent.

Distracted, upset, and unable to make up her mind, Katherine rushes off by herself, wandering absently through the paths and corridors of the University until she finds herself finally in a deserted alcove near the library, where she pours out her troubles in a long monologue.

But the alcove is not quite so deserted as it seems at first. Placed in three shadowy niches toward the back are marble busts of Plato, Voltaire, and Freud. As Katherine proceeds to outline her dilemma, the busts burst into life, and each sings his advice to her. Plato counsels her to stick with Peter and "keep it Platonic," while Voltaire suggests she keep both husband and lover, in the French fashion. But it is Freud who convinces her in the end, when he tells her to throw off her inhibitions, follow her impulse, and "run away, run away." Stopping only long enough to write Peter a farewell note, Katherine prepares to go off on the mountain escapade.

By three in the morning, the reunion celebration has reached its climax, with the sons of Harrison alternately quarreling and weeping on one another's shoulders. Despite his usual coolness, even Peter is feeling a little lonely and maudlin and on edge.

Once again, Christopher tracks him down. This time she hands him Katherine's farewell note and a copy of the book *The Day Before Spring*. In the note, Katherine explains that Peter will only be able to understand her behavior if he reads the book. Under the circumstances, Christopher manages to persuade Peter to go with her for a drive and a couple of drinks. But that will be all there will be to it, he insists—and she reluctantly agrees. To seal the date, they sing the ironic love duet "A Jug of Wine" (see p. 28).

Then Peter settles down to read the book. In his mind's eye, he envisages the idyllic mountain retreat that Alex has described, the arrival of the happy couple, and their ecstatic reaction to the lovely setting. He imagines them singing, along with the other "newlywed" couples at the lodge, a hymn to their newfound joy—"I Love You This Morning" (see p. 33).

The scene goes on in Peter's imagination, becoming more detailed and more unbearable with each passing second. He imagines Katherine and Alex becoming more and more intimate. With increasing distaste, he reads out the heavily romantic dialogue that Alex has written for the scene in his book. Suddenly, just at the point where Alex and Katherine are about to enter the lodge (in the book and in his vivid mental picture), Peter slams down the book, exclaiming: "What does he think he's doing? That's my wife!"

Meantime, all is not going quite so idyllically as planned with the runaway couple. Alex's car has broken down in very nearly the same spot as it did ten years before, and the pair is stranded miserably on a lonely country road. Alex goes off to get help and Katherine, cold, impatient, and alone, sings bitterly of her twice-foiled adventure—"This Is My Holiday" (see p. 36).

Alex has not yet returned when Peter drives up in Christopher's car. He rushes to Katherine, intent on

The elopement scene is re-created in Antony Tudor's choreography. The Alex of the book (Hugh Laing) urges the fictional Katherine (Mary Ellen Moylan) off the stage as Peter (John Archer) takes Christopher (Patricia Marshall) in his arms. [PHOTO VANDAMM.]

talking her into coming back to him. Just as he has almost persuaded her, Alex returns and the discussion begins all over again.

Peter's argument is that Alex's whole approach to life, his romanticism and his irresponsibility, is non-sensical. Not only is his dream far removed from reality, but if he and Katherine ever did manage to escape into the world he has described in the book, they would find it unutterably dreary. For Katherine, Alex represents nothing but a tedious sophomoric retrogression, like the reunion weekend itself.

Finally Gerald arrives, to help with the car. After listening to the discussion for a while, he swings over to Peter's side and delivers the *coup de grâce* in the form of a realistic, detailed description of what Alex's day-to-day life and personality are really like.

Katherine sees the light and agrees to go back with Peter. Gerald is naturally out of a job, but he is just as happy to concentrate all his energies on continuing the pursuit of Christopher...while Alex prepares to set off for China, to write a novel about a boy and girl who elope in a ricksha.

The Day Before Spring

Copyright © 1945 by Leo Feist, Inc.
Chappell & Co., Inc., New York, N.Y., Publisher and Owner of allied rights for the United States.

God's Green World

Copyright © 1945 by Leo Feist, Inc.
Chappell & Co., Inc., New York, N.Y., Publisher and Owner of allied rights for the United States.

My Love Is a Married Man

Moderato

Copyright © 1946 by Leo Feist, Inc.
Chappell & Co., Inc., New York, N.Y., Publisher and Owner of allied rights for the United States.

true to his wife.___ My love is a mar - ried man.___

___ How of - ten I dream and plan___ That he'd

climb on my ca - ra - van.___ I'm a child-ish dope;___

___ Will it hap - pen? Nope!___ He's not that kind of a mar-

A Jug of Wine

Moderato

mf

Em7   Cm   Dm7   C6   PETER: *(Spoken)* Any place

Could we take a jour-ney to the moon?

mp   Em

that has a good saloon.   Am   Am7   PETER: Any place that

Could we ride a rock-et to a star?

F6

has a friendly bar.   C   C7   F

Could we find a world of strange de-

Copyright © 1945 by Leo Feist, Inc.
Chappell & Co., Inc., New York, N.Y., Publisher and Owner of allied rights for the United States.

I Love You This Morning

Copyright © 1945 by Leo Feist, Inc.
Chappell & Co., Inc., New York, N.Y., Publisher and Owner of allied rights for the United States.

This Is My Holiday

Copyright © 1945 by Leo Feist, Inc.
Chappell & Co., Inc., New York, N.Y., Publisher and Owner of allied rights for the United States.

BRIGADOON

OPENED MARCH 13, 1947, AT THE ZIEGFELD THEATRE—581 PERFORMANCES

Book and Lyrics by ALAN JAY LERNER ❧ *Music by* FREDERICK LOEWE

PRODUCED BY CHERYL CRAWFORD

DANCE AND MUSICAL NUMBERS BY AGNES DE MILLE

PRODUCTION STAGED BY ROBERT LEWIS

SCENERY DESIGNED BY OLIVER SMITH

COSTUMES DESIGNED BY DAVID FFOLKES

MUSICAL DIRECTOR: FRANZ ALLERS

VOCAL ARRANGEMENTS BY MR. LOEWE

ORCHESTRATIONS BY TED ROYAL

LIGHTING BY PEGGY CLARK

ORIGINAL CAST

[IN ORDER OF APPEARANCE]

TOMMY ALBRIGHT	DAVID BROOKS
JEFF DOUGLAS	GEORGE KEANE
ARCHIE BEATON	ELLIOTT SULLIVAN
HARRY BEATON	JAMES MITCHELL
FISHMONGER	BUNTY KELLEY
ANGUS MacGUFFIE	JULES RACINE
SANDY DEAN	HAYES GORDON
ANDREW MacLAREN	EDWARD CULLEN
FIONA MacLAREN	MARION BELL
JEAN MacLAREN	VIRGINIA BOSLER
MEG BROCKIE	PAMELA BRITTON
CHARLIE DALRYMPLE	LEE SULLIVAN
MAGGIE ANDERSON	LIDIJA FRANKLIN
MR. LUNDIE	WILLIAM HANSEN
SWORD DANCERS	{ ROLAND GUERARD / GEORGE DRAKE }
FRANK	JOHN PAUL
JANE ASHTON	FRANCES CHARLES
BAGPIPERS	{ JAMES MacFADDEN / ARTHUR HORN }
STUART DALRYMPLE	DELBERT ANDERSON
MacGREGOR	EARL REDDING

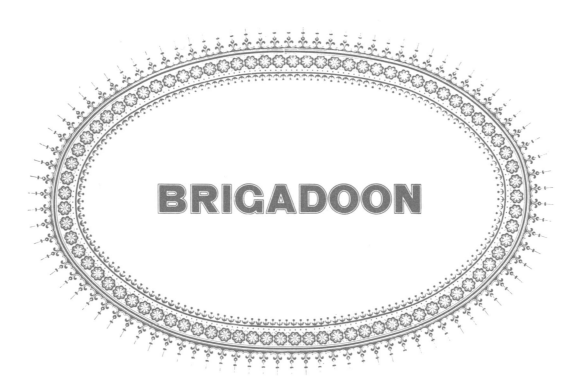

BRIGADOON

BRIGADOON DESERVES, AND HOLDS, A VERY SPE-
cial position in the Lerner and Loewe canon. For,
whatever the merits of the team's previous collaborations—and in *The Day Before Spring* the merits had been
considerable—the new musical that opened at the Ziegfeld on March 13, 1947, was incontestably different
from, and superior to, everything that had come before it.

For the first time, the authors had succeeded in fusing
the new techniques and ideas that were to characterize
all their later works into a fully developed, coherent
dramatic whole. *Brigadoon* was something new under
the Broadway sun. It owed a debt, of course, to the in-
novations of Rodgers and Hammerstein, but to what it
derived from their work it added at least as much that
was entirely original.

Brigadoon was an immediate smash hit, the first that
Lerner and Loewe had. The critics were vigorous and
unanimous in their praises. John Chapman of the *News*
put forward the thesis that now the American musical

theater had outstripped legitimate drama not only in
charm but in serious technique and interest as well.
The end of the season saw an embarrassing division
among the members of the Drama Critics Circle as to
whether *Brigadoon* should be allowed to qualify in the
voting for the year's best "play." It wasn't allowed,
and it had to be content with awards for best musical,
lyrics, score, choreography, and female lead (Marion
Bell).

Behind all the kudos lay not only an immense amount
of work by both men, but also a strictly arranged pattern of procedure, worked out mainly by Lerner, which
would be used again, with slight variations, in the preparation of *Paint Your Wagon, My Fair Lady, Gigi,* and
Camelot.

The first step in the work on *Brigadoon* was an ex-
haustive, painstaking study of the history, manners,
and customs of the highland Scots in the eighteenth
century. Lerner began this digging with a plot idea in

mind, but he developed the idea very largely in detail, he later reported, during the course of his researches. He was, for the first time, indulging the passion for accuracy, for the *rightness* of mood and tone, that obsessed him in all his later work.

Perhaps a more crucial element in the long evolution of the script was Lerner's concern that the central theme—the contrast between the complications and feverish distractions of the urban twentieth century with the apparently idyllic, though provincial and remote, simplicity of a rural eighteenth-century village—should be treated with fundamental seriousness.

In a preface he wrote some years later for the published version of *Paint Your Wagon*, Lerner returned to the problem of originality in the musical theater, strongly advocating the adaptation of already existing literary material. The effort to evolve original plots when there was so much splendid material available, he argued, called for an expense of energy and spirit that could be far better employed in dealing with the specific problems of the musical stage. This was advice he had not followed himself with *Brigadoon* but was to adopt and hold to in the future.

When the book of *Brigadoon* was finally ready, Loewe set out to compose a score that would match Lerner's script for accuracy of style and mood. The problem was to devise a musical setting that would be unmistakably Scottish while at the same time avoiding the temptation to rely on the screech of bagpipes and the all-too-facile rhythms of the reel.

Loewe briefly considered the notion of visiting Scotland for inspiration. In the end, he rejected it. He had never been there, and he has not been there since. He argued that the only relevant tools for the job were a sound musical training and one's own intuition. If those tools did not make the task possible, nothing else would.

The result of his efforts was one of the most successful scores he has written. It achieved the Scottish tone without parodying it. A source of special satisfaction to the composer was the ballad "Almost Like Being in Love," which soon established itself as a popular hit in its own right, a feat that few of his songs, despite their huge popularity on Broadway and in original-cast recordings, have accomplished.

James Mitchell wears his kilt as Harry Beaton.
[COURTESY CHERYL CRAWFORD]

Pamela Britton as Meg Brockie sings "My Mother's Weddin' Day" in Act II. [PHOTO VANDAMM]

Much of the credit for the ultimate success of the show was due to its producer, Cheryl Crawford of the Group Theatre. Four other producers had turned down the script before she saw it. But she had immediately recognized in it the concrete expression of many ideas she had long entertained for the musical stage, and she had set to work on its production straightaway. A first problem was financial backing and, oddly enough in the light of the success of *The Day Before Spring*, it proved nearly insurmountable.

After money was finally found, the authors set about casting the show for Broadway. It was the general feeling that young, relatively unknown actors should be used—an intuition that paid off handsomely in the outstanding performances of Marion Bell, David Brooks, and Pamela Britton. Agnes de Mille planned what was for her a new sort of choreography, nondramatic in essence, based on the classic Scotch forms but heightened to achieve an effect of deeply emotional folk ritual. Certain dramatic scenes, such as the chase and the fight at the wedding, were stylized pantomime, in rhythm and to music. The chase with its snatches of sung dialogue interspersed with violent action approached a new lyric form.

Offsetting the initial difficulty in finding financial backing, Miss Crawford contrived to open the show with over $400,000 in advance booking, a figure even more impressive then than now. But the show hardly needed it. The morning after the opening, everyone involved had the satisfaction of reading notices that ran to such phrases as "a musical play of rare delight . . . enchanting . . . unquestionably the most distinguished new musical show of the year."

Brigadoon—and Lerner and Loewe—had come to stay.

At THE OPENING CURTAIN, two American hunters are wandering, hopelessly lost, in a forest in the Scottish Highlands at five o'clock on a misty morning. The younger man, Tommy, is handsome and sensitive, while the other, Jeff, is somewhat coarser-grained and given to irony. Neither of them seems like much of an outdoor type.

As their map seems to offer them no useful clues to their whereabouts, they are preparing to settle in for the night. They talk somewhat aimlessly, mainly about Jane, the girl Tommy is engaged to in New York, though it appears that he has little enthusiasm for his approaching marriage. Their talk is interrupted by faint, faraway music, which gradually defines itself as the song "Brigadoon" (see p. 50). At the same time, a village emerges into view in the valley below them—in a spot where none had appeared before and where none is located on the map. The two men set out toward it.

The scene shifts to MacConnachy Square in Brigadoon, where there is a lively market fair in progress, attended by all the villagers. Among them are a Mr. MacLaren and his daughters Fiona and Jean, who are all busily engaged in making preparations for Jean's wedding, scheduled for this same afternoon. One of their errands takes them to Archie Beaton's woolengoods stall, where Jean encounters Archie's son Harry, one of her rejected suitors. Harry is miserable and furious over the prospect of the wedding, but, as Jean is obviously in love with her proposed groom and thoroughly pleased about the way things are going, she manages to laugh off Harry's last-minute intervention.

Meanwhile, Fiona has fallen into a discussion of love and marriage with her friend Meg, an almost incredibly lusty girl, who is dying to find a man—any man. Fiona violently disagrees with Meg's point of view, and she explains why in the song "Waitin' for My Dearie" (see p. 52).

Not long after, Tommy and Jeff wander into the square, showing signs of bewilderment at what they see. The citizens of Brigadoon, however, seem just as much disoriented by the Americans' modern clothes and vocabularies as Tommy and Jeff are by the natives' quaint clothes and accents. But in spite of the sense of strangeness, there is friendliness on both sides—and something more than simple friendliness, too, in Meg's reaction to Jeff, whom she immediately spirits off to "rest" at her place.

Tommy is left alone with Fiona, and they are soon involved in a pleasant conversation, though Jeff is increasingly disturbed by the oddity of her reactions and by her apparent isolation from everything in the outside world. As they are talking, Jean's fiancé, Charlie Dalrymple, arrives. In the course of discussing the day's plans, he remarks that he is grateful "to Mr. Forsythe for postponin' the miracle," and when Tommy asks Fiona for an explanation of what he means, she tries to pass it off. She drags Tommy off to do an errand with her, and while they are gone, Charlie sings of his love for Jean and his desire to settle down with her after a fickle youth. From now on, he asserts, "I'll Go Home with Bonnie Jean."

When Tommy and Fiona return, their conversation has got onto the subject of his own prospective marriage. Unlike Charlie, Tommy confides, he faces it with deep misgivings. Fiona is shocked by his confession, but he counters with the observation that there are plenty of strange things about her and Brigadoon as well—particularly the "miracle," which she still refuses to explain.

Still, in spite of their misunderstandings, there is an obvious attraction growing between Fiona and Tommy. She says he may come to the wedding in the afternoon, and as she is about to go off to gather heather to decorate the cottage, Tommy invites himself along—and Fiona accepts—in the song "The Heather on the Hill" (see p. 56).

There follows an interlude in Meg's shed, to which she has brought Jeff, fatigued after his long night outdoors and interested in nothing but a restorative nap. Meg has other ideas. She tries feminine blandishments, then guile, and is about to resort to force, when Jeff forestalls her by asking for the story of her life. To his request she responds with an account of her many, many loves, all of whom got away, in the song "The Love of My Life" (see p. 60).

At the same time, back at the MacLarens' cottage, preparations for the wedding feast go forward: Jean's trousseau is being sorted and packed by her friends and Jean is upstairs dressing. Charlie arrives for one last look at his bride before the ceremony, but Mr. MacLaren forbids this, on the grounds that it would bring bad luck. So Charlie is forced to content himself with singing, from downstairs, the wistful, romantic ballad "Come to Me, Bend to Me" (see p. 65).

Soon Fiona and Tommy arrive back from their after-

Oliver Smith's sketch for the scene below, outside the kirk of Brigadoon. At the close of the marriage ceremony, Jean (Virginia Bosler) and Charlie (Lee Sullivan) begin the wedding dance. [PHOTO VANDAMM]

noon of heather gathering. Jeff also returns, fresh from what has turned out to be a most rewarding spell with Meg after all. It is clear to Jeff that the attraction between Tommy and Fiona has ripened over the afternoon, an observation that they shortly confirm in the duet "Almost Like Being in Love" (see p. 68).

Fiona goes upstairs to help her sister dress, and Tommy picks up the MacLaren family Bible and begins thumbing idly through it. Suddenly he makes a discovery that reduces him to stuttering incredulity. The last entries recorded are those of Jean's and Fiona's births—in 1723 and 1729! The wedding of Jean Mac-Laren with Charlie Dalrymple is already entered—for 1747! Fiona comes downstairs just after Tommy and Jeff have made their discovery, and when they face her with it, she finally agrees to take them to see Mr. Lundie, the only man who can properly explain the mysteries of Brigadoon.

Tommy, Jeff, and Fiona find Mr. Lundie, who turns out to be a kindly old schoolmaster, reading on his front porch. Somewhat to Fiona's surprise, he seems quite happy to tell the strangers the story. It appears that in 1747 the Scottish highlands were afflicted with a plague of witches, who had ravaged much of the countryside and would soon, it was thought, fall on Brigadoon. A holy man in the town named Forsythe resolved to ask the Lord for a miracle that would free Brigadoon not only from the immediate threat posed by the witches but also from all the periodic disasters and upheavals that befell the world. After thinking through quite carefully what precisely he should ask for, he finally prayed that each night when the people of Brigadoon went to bed, the village would disappear into the mists, and that it would reappear only once, for a day each time, every hundred years.

The miracle would go on uninterruptedly forever, the people of Brigadoon living out their normal lives, one day in a century. No one could participate in the miracle unless he were one of the original inhabitants or a stranger who had truly fallen in love with someone from Brigadoon, and the spell would be broken only if one of the natives left the village of his own accord. The miracle had been delayed twenty-four hours—two centuries or two days before—so that Charlie Dalrymple could return from the University at Edinburgh to marry Jean MacLaren.

As Mr. Lundie finishes his story, the first strains of the wedding music are heard, and everyone goes off to attend the brief, moving ceremony. Then, just as the wedding party is about to begin, Harry Beaton, the rejected suitor, turns up drunk and obviously enraged. Seizing a sword, he begins to brawl with one of the guests and is just prevented from injuring someone by Tommy's wrenching the weapon from his grasp. Defeated but still defiant, Harry announces that he intends to break the miracle by leaving Brigadoon and thereupon rushes off.

The second act opens with the entire male population of the village hunting Harry through the woods. The hunt comes to a sudden dramatic conclusion when one of the parties discovers the boy's dead body. He appears to have fallen somehow, hit his head, and died from the wound. There is general relief and rejoicing at the fact that Brigadoon has been saved. The men decide not to reveal Harry's death even to his father Archie till after the wedding celebration, and they simply take the body back to the Beaton cabin.

Returning to meet the women and Archie, the men announce that Harry has not escaped but that he is injured and has been put to rest at home. Tommy, back from the hunt, meets Fiona once more. Their feeling for one another is quite fully confirmed by now, and Fiona is immensely relieved that Tommy has not taken the opportunity of the hunt to slip out of Brigadoon himself. Tommy has become entirely aware of what he feels for Fiona and expresses it in the song "There But for You Go I" (see p. 71).

Shortly afterward, the whole town is gathered in the glen to resume the interrupted wedding celebration. Meg opens the proceedings with a full account of a similar affair, "My Mother's Weddin' Day" (see p. 75), a story she knows well, since she was there to see it. The party goes gaily on through a series of highland dances. But it is suddenly interrupted by the arrival of Archie Beaton, bearing the body of his dead son. The villagers suspend their merrymaking for a few moments while an almost shockingly perfunctory funeral service is performed over the dead boy, and then—within seconds after it is completed—they return to their celebration.

During a lull in the festivities, Tommy informs Jeff that he has made up his mind to stay in Brigadoon, an announcement that appalls Jeff, who immediately attempts to dissuade his friend. Jeff says that Brigadoon is nothing but a will-o'-the-wisp; that it would be unthinkable for Tommy to commit his life to a fairy tale. As proof of the total unreality of the situation, Jeff confesses that it was he who accidentally killed Harry Beaton and asserts that the incident had no effect on him whatsoever: it was as though he had simply wiped out a figment of his own imagination.

Tommy's resolve is shaken, and he gives in to Jeff's argument. In a final scene with Fiona, he tells her that he will have to leave Brigadoon, and they sing one last duet together, assuring one another of their enduring love, "From This Day On" (see p. 78).

The following scene takes place in a New York bar four months later. Cozily ensconced in his favorite spot, Jeff is bewailing the fact that Tommy quit his job and disappeared the month before. In the midst of Jeff's explanation, Tommy himself enters. He explains to his friend that since their day in Brigadoon he has been like a haunted man, that he cannot get the idea of the village or of Fiona out of his head, and that even his month-long retreat has not enabled him to forget.

Eventually, Tommy's fiancée Jane enters. She is an attractive American girl, but nervous and brittle, an absolute contrast to Fiona. As she begins to discuss her everyday preoccupations, including plans for the wedding, Tommy dreams off again and again, his mind harking back to Fiona's voice, singing the songs of Brigadoon. Something suddenly snaps into place and he makes up his mind to return to Scotland.

In the final scene, Tommy and Jeff are once more wandering in the Highlands in the neighborhood of Brigadoon, which has, of course, disappeared again into the mists. Tommy is not quite sure what the object of his trip is, but he tells Jeff that he would now take his chances on living in Brigadoon, if only it were possible. At the last instant, just as the two men are about to turn away, there is a break in the mist and the song "Brigadoon" is faintly heard, while Mr. Lundie appears, yawning, as if from nowhere. He stretches his hand out to Tommy and leads him away from the twentieth century to the village and the girl he has finally proved he truly loves.

The management announces with pride...

Brigadoon

Copyright © 1947 by Alan Jay Lerner and Frederick Loewe
World rights assigned to Chappell & Co., Inc. World rights assigned to and controlled by Sam Fox Publishing Company, Inc.

Waitin' for My Dearie

Copyright © 1947 by Alan Jay Lerner and Frederick Loewe
World rights assigned to Chappell & Co., Inc. World rights assigned to and controlled by Sam Fox Publishing Company, Inc.

The Heather on the Hill

Copyright © 1947 by Alan Jay Lerner and Frederick Loewe
World rights assigned to Chappell & Co., Inc. World rights assigned to and controlled by Sam Fox Publishing Company, Inc.

Liltingly

The mist of May is in the gloam-in', and all the clouds are hold-in' still

So take my hand and let's go roam-in' through the

heath-er on the hill. The morn-in' dew is blink-in'

yon-der, there's laz-y mu-sic in the rill

The Love of My Life

Copyright © 1947 by Alan Jay Lerner and Frederick Loewe
World rights assigned to Chappell & Co., Inc. World rights assigned to and controlled by Sam Fox Publishing Company, Inc.

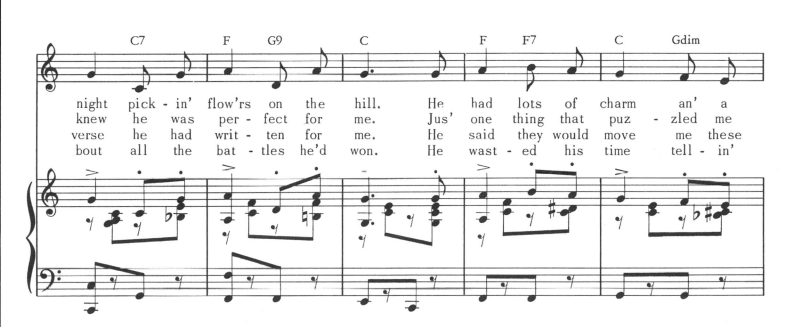

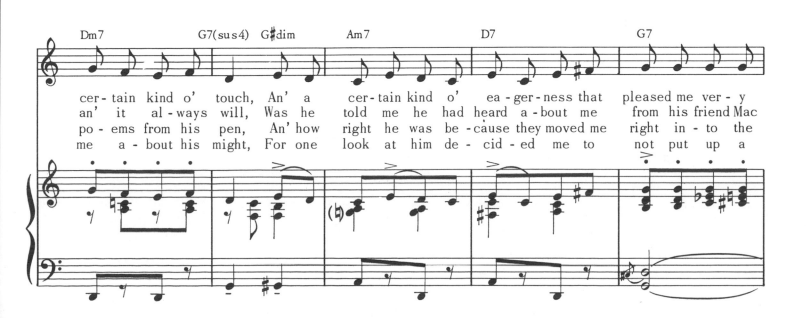

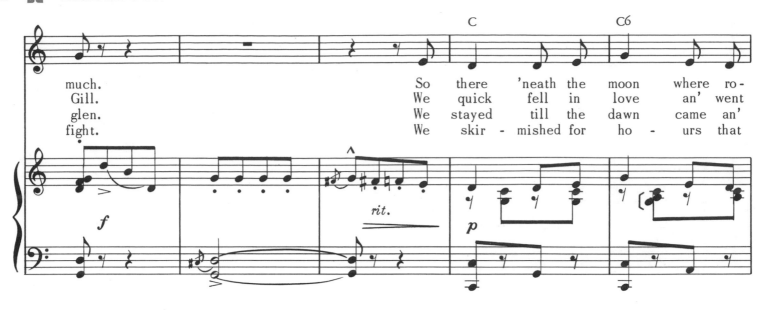

much.
Gill.
glen.
fight.

So there 'neath the moon where ro-
We quick fell in love an' went
We stayed till the dawn came an'
We skir-mished for ho-urs that

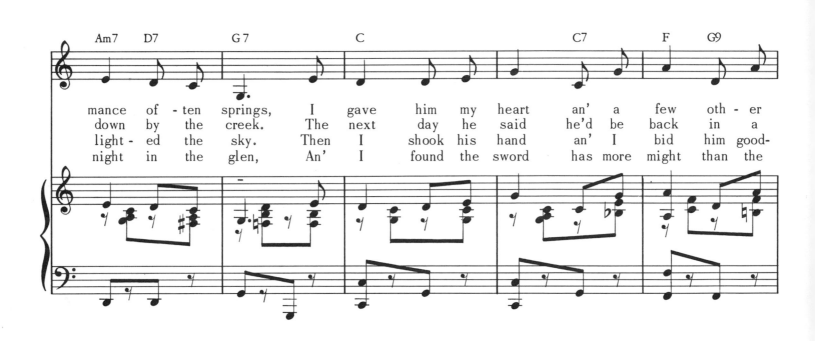

mance of-ten springs, I gave him my heart an' a few oth-er
down by the creek. The next day he said he'd be back in a
light-ed the sky. Then I shook his hand an' I bid him good-
night in the glen, An' I found the sword has more might than the

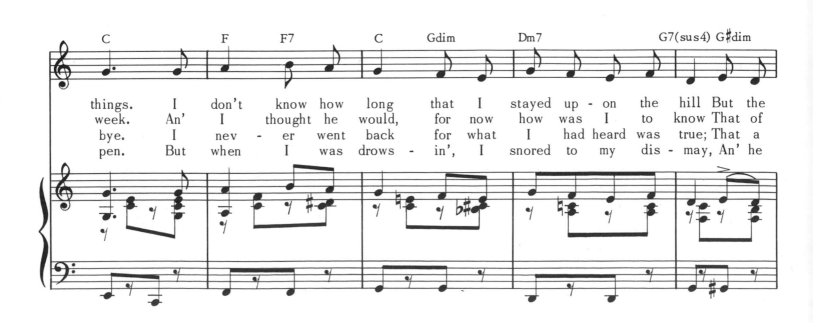

things. I don't know how long that I stayed up-on the hill But the
week. An' I thought he would, for now how was I to know That of
bye. I nev-er went back for what I had heard was true; That a
pen. But when I was drows-in', I snored to my dis-may, An' he

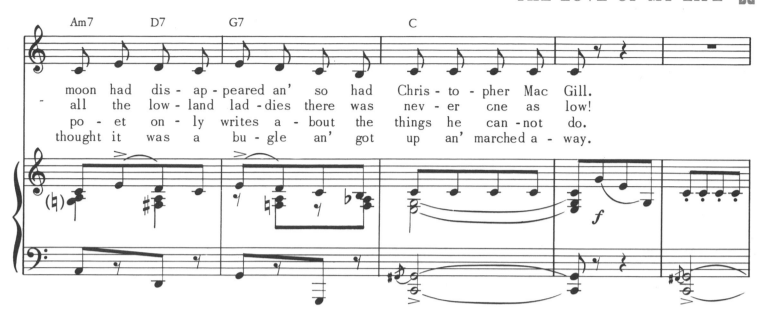

moon had dis - ap - peared an' so had Chris - to - pher Mac Gill.
all the low - land lad - dies there was nev - er one as low!
po - et on - ly writes a - bout the things he can - not do.
thought it was a bu - gle an' got up an' marched a - way.

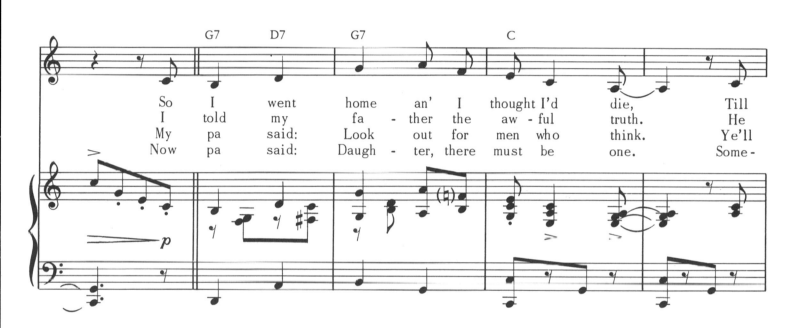

So I went home an' I thought I'd die, Till
I told my fa - ther the aw - ful truth. He
My pa said: Look out for men who think. Ye'll
Now pa said: Daugh - ter, there must be one. Some -

fa - ther said: Make an - oth - er try.___ So out I
said: What diff - 'rence? Ye've got your youth.___ So out I
be more cer - tain with men who drink.___ So out I
one who's true or too old to run.___ So I'm still

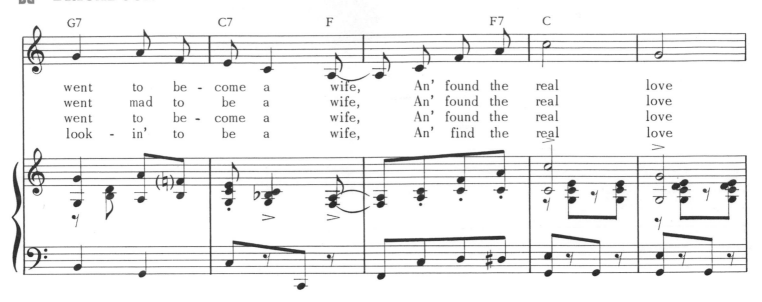

went to be - come a wife, An' found the real love
went mad to be a wife, An' found the real love
went to be - come a wife, An' found the real love
look - in' to be a wife, An' find the real love

1. 2. 3.

of my life.
of my life.
of my life. 2. He
of 3. Oh,
4. Oh,

4.

my life. _____

Come to Me, Bend to Me

Slowly, with feeling

Be - cause they've told me I can't be -
near me so ye can

Copyright © 1947 by Alan Jay Lerner and Frederick Loewe
World rights assigned to Chappell & Co., Inc. World rights assigned to and controlled by Sam Fox Publishing Company, Inc.

Darl - in', my darl - in', 'tis all I can say, just

Come to me, bend to me kiss me good day!

Give me your lips an' don't take them a -

way.   Come dear - ie way.

Almost Like Being in Love

Copyright © 1947 by Alan Jay Lerner and Frederick Loewe
World rights assigned to Chappell & Co., Inc. World rights assigned to and controlled by Sam Fox Publishing Company, Inc.

There But for You Go I

Copyright © 1947 by Alan Jay Lerner and Frederick Loewe
World rights assigned to Chappell & Co., Inc. World rights assigned to and controlled by Sam Fox Publishing Company, Inc.

My Mother's Weddin' Day

Allegro comodo

Now if ye think this wed-din' day went jus' a bit a-miss,__ Then I will tell ye 'bout a wed-din' far more daft than this.__ The lad in-volved turned out to be no oth-er but my pa.__ An' by the strang-est bit o' luck, the wo-man was my ma.__ Mac-

Copyright © 1947 by Alan Jay Lerner and Frederick Loewe
World rights assigned to Chappell & Co., Inc. World rights assigned to and controlled by Sam Fox Publishing Company, Inc.

up the road came Ed Mac Keen, With half the town of
while the men were dip - pin' in, The la - dies start - ed

A -ber-deen
on the gin

Aye, ev - 'ry one was on the scene At her moth -er's wed-din' day.
An' soon the room be - gan to spin At her moth -er's wed-din' day.

2. At

3. Then all of a sudden the liquor was gone;
   The gin an' the whiskey an' all.
   An' all of a sudden the weddin' affair
   Had become a bonnie brawl.
   For Pete MacGraw an' Joe MacPhee
   Began to fight for May MacGee,
   While May MacGee an' Sam MacKee
   Were a-wooin' in the hall.
   So cold an' stiff was John MacVay
   They used 'im for a servin' tray.
   For ev'ryone was blithe an' gay.
   At her mother's weddin' day.

4. The people were lyin' all over the room,
   A-lookin' as if they were dead.
   Then mother uncovered the minister quick,
   An' she told 'im, "Go ahead."
   Then pa kneeled down on Bill MacRae,
   An' mother kneeled on Jock MacKay;
   The preacher stood on John MacVay;
   An' that's how my ma was wed.
   It was a sight beyond compare,
   I ought to know for I was there.
   There never was a day as rare
   As her mother's weddin' day!

From This Day On

Copyright © 1947 by Alan Jay Lerner and Frederick Loewe
World rights assigned to Chappell & Co., Inc. World rights assigned to and controlled by Sam Fox Publishing Company, Inc.

Paint Your Wagon

OPENED NOVEMBER 12, 1951, AT THE SHUBERT THEATRE—289 PERFORMANCES

Book and Lyrics by ALAN JAY LERNER ❖ *Music by* FREDERICK LOEWE

PRODUCED BY CHERYL CRAWFORD

DIRECTED BY DANIEL MANN

DANCES AND MUSICAL ENSEMBLES BY AGNES DE MILLE

SCENERY DESIGNED BY OLIVER SMITH

COSTUMES DESIGNED BY MOTLEY

ORCHESTRA AND CHORUS CONDUCTED BY FRANZ ALLERS

LIGHTING BY PEGGY CLARK

ORCHESTRATIONS BY TED ROYAL

MUSIC FOR DANCES ARRANGED BY TRUDE RITTMAN

PRODUCTION ASSOCIATE: BEA LAWRENCE

ORIGINAL CAST

[IN ORDER OF APPEARANCE]

WALT	BERT MATTHEWS
JENNIFER RUMSON	OLGA SAN JUAN
SALEM TRUMBULL	RALPH BUNKER
JASPER	TED THURSTON
BEN RUMSON	JAMES BARTON
STEVE BULLNACK	RUFUS SMITH
PETE BILLINGS	JAMES MITCHELL
CHERRY	KAY MEDFORD
JAKE WHIPPANY	ROBERT PENN
MIKE MOONEY	JOHN RANDOLPH
DOCTOR NEWCOMB	DAVID THOMAS
SING ·YUY	TOM AI
LEE ZEN	CHUN-TAO CHENG
EDGAR CROCKER	RICHARD AHERNE
SANDY TWIST	JARED REED
REUBEN SLOANE	GORDON DILWORTH
JULIO VALVERAS	TONY BAVAAR
JACOB WOODLING	JOSH WHEELER
ELIZABETH WOODLING	MARIJANE MARICLE
SARAH WOODLING	JAN SHERWOOD
DUTCHIE	BERT MATTHEWS
CARMELLITA	LORRAINE HAVERCROFT
YVONNE SOREL	GEMZE DE LAPPE
SUZANNE DUVAL	MARY BURR
ELSIE	GISELLA SVETLIK
RAYMOND JANNEY	GORDON DILWORTH
ROCKY	JAMES TARBUTTON
JOE	NORMAN WEISE
JACK	DELBERT ANDERSON
ED	EDGAR THOMPSON
BILL	NEWTON SULLIVAN
SAM	FEODORE TEDICK
JOHANSEN	JOHN ANDERSON

Paint Your Wagon

THERE ARE AT LEAST TWO MAJOR CATEGORIES OF Lerner and Loewe fans. The first, and larger, owes its primary devotion to *My Fair Lady*. The second, though smaller, is a good deal better organized and more fervent. While generously conceding to *My Fair Lady* all its merits, it goes on quietly practicing the cult of *Paint Your Wagon*.

It is a curious phenomenon. *Paint Your Wagon* was by no means as successful as were *My Fair Lady* and *Camelot,* and it did not even run as long as *Brigadoon,* which preceded it. In addition, it had a mixed critical reception. And yet no other show that Lerner and Loewe have written has inspired quite such intense and devoted partisanship in its admirers.

The cause may well lie in the passion that its authors, particularly Lerner, put into it. He had been fascinated with the history of the Gold Rush for years, and, though he put the project off several times, he remained convinced that a realistic portrayal of the American West, free of false glamor and deriving from the hard facts of pioneer life, would make a magnificent subject for a musical play.

He got down to intensive research while *Brigadoon* was still enjoying its long, successful run. The digging had already begun while the earlier show was in the works. It took more than three years, Lerner calculated later, and it led down one blind alley after another. The trouble with the great bulk of the secondary material Lerner read was an inadmissible romanticism. Frontier crime and frontier sex were the two leading themes, and nowhere did it seem possible to learn about the everyday tone of Gold Rush life. Bret Harte was the writer who had originally inspired Lerner's interest in the subject. But little of the other fiction that he discovered helped to supplement the picture he had got from Harte.

The break came when Lerner stumbled across an historical account of the Comstock community between 1848 and 1853. In it, Lerner found many of his hunches confirmed and much new, workable material as well.

Oddly enough, it turned out that crime was next to unknown in the community and that what little there was was dealt with swiftly, cruelly, and effectively.

And far from being centers of untrammeled licentiousness, Lerner discovered, the gold towns suffered from one overwhelming inconvenience—a woman shortage both chronic and acute. A second major problem at Comstock was the friction between Anglo-Saxon and Mexican miners, which was unilaterally resolved by the more or less complete exclusion of the Mexican minority.

Underlying all the specific difficulties was, of course, the fundamental hazardousness and uncertainty of mining life, the dependence on the lode's holding out, the constant migrations from one strike to the next, the high price of necessities, and the perpetual availability of high-stakes gambling, which led to the quick dissipation of overnight fortunes. Above everything else, Lerner was impressed by the "robustness, vitality, and cockeyed courage" of the community as a whole under these conditions. Around this theme, supported by the facts of the Mexican problem and the woman shortage, Lerner decided to construct his play. "The show was a brute to write," he commented shortly after the opening; "there was far too much material."

In the material that did find its way into the final version were a number of incidents taken nearly verbatim from the Comstock records. The appearance of a Mormon stranger and his two wives, and the decision to give the man a stake on condition that he consent to put up one wife at public auction, for example, are not factual, but the courtroom scene and the discovery of gold are.

Lerner's concern for the exact details of mood and tone would, of course, have been largely wasted had it not been matched by an equal scrupulousness in the execution of the score and especially of the choreography. The musical problems that the script presented to Loewe were comparable with those raised by *Brigadoon*. He was required to work in an idiom that was foreign to his own musical background but deeply familiar to most of his audiences. And, of course, there was no possibility of visiting the California of the 1850s for inspiration or atmosphere. His only recourse was to study the music of the period and, ultimately, to re-create its mood in his own terms. It has since become a source of amazement that a European by birth should have been able to compose one of the most stirring Western scores in existence.

It turned out to be one of the most difficult assignments he had ever tackled. He wrote nearly forty songs before settling on the dozen that would appear in the show. One measure of his success—and one of his proudest achievements—is the fact that "They Call the Wind Maria" has been accepted into the tiny, exclusive company of "folk songs"; though written in cold blood by a single hand, it is admired and regularly played by folk purists.

Agnes de Mille was once again chosen as choreographer, and even the reviews that dealt least charitably with the show as a whole gave her credit for topping her earlier splendid performance with *Brigadoon*. For the second time, too, Cheryl Crawford took over as producer, and, as in *Brigadoon*, the cast was recruited mainly from among young, bright, relatively unknown actors. Olga San Juan, who played the ingenue Jennifer, was, according to the consensus, the standout among them.

The show was lavishly produced, costing something over $200,000 before it reached Broadway. It had the classic rocky seven weeks on the road and was largely rewritten out of town, mainly in Boston. It was greeted in New York by some of the most adulatory reviews the authors have ever received and by some of the least friendly as well. It settled down to a solid run—not a smash hit by *My Fair Lady* standards, but a respectable one by any other—and it won *Variety's* Poll of New York Drama Critics for the best score of 1951–52.

One postscript to the story of *Paint Your Wagon* was a source of peculiar satisfaction to the authors. By and large, their songs had, and have since, proved a little too intricate and sophisticated to become established as popular hits in their own right, despite the huge successes of all their original-cast albums. Only one song from *Brigadoon* had turned the trick. Now *Paint Your Wagon* furnished two others in "I Talk to the Trees" and "They Call the Wind Maria." (In an interview in 1959, Lerner expressed his pleasure at having written two or three lyrics that had been capable of migrating from Shubert Alley to Tin Pan Alley.)

THE ACTION OF THE PLAY begins with the discovery of gold at Rumson Creek, California, in 1853.

Within hours after the event, the news has spread all over the West. Farmers lay down their plows, schoolteachers desert their classrooms, gamblers pack up their cards and dice, and wives and girls are left with a

As Al Hirschfeld saw the principals of *Paint Your Wagon* in *The New York Times. Left to right:* Mary Burr (Suzanne), James Mitchell (Pete), Gemze de Lappe (Yvonne), James Barton (Ben), Olga San Juan (Jennifer), and Tony Bavaar (Julio).

kiss and a promise. No one can say quite where he is going or just what he will find when he arrives, but the wanderlust has mastered them all, as has the lust for gold. "All I know is," they chorus, "I'm on My Way" (see p. 91).

Two months later Rumson is settled into the pattern of a booming Gold Rush camp, with the miners' shacks centering around an improvised general store, where a cagey old New Englander, Salem Trumbull, sells eggs at fifty-two cents apiece and picks and shovels for seventeen dollars the set. Though gold is being uncovered steadily enough for the four hundred miners, the life is still rough and tedious. The functions of mayor, arbitrator, and keeper of the peace have fallen to Ben Rumson, who made the original strike, and his task is not an easy one.

The men are bored to distraction, restless, and particularly disturbed by the lack of available women. In fact, the only woman in the camp is Ben's pretty sixteen-year-old daughter, who is, of course, out of bounds to everyone. To make matters worse, Jennifer is entirely unconscious of the effect her presence has on the miners, and, as a result, she behaves more provocatively than she should. One afternoon, the miners become so jumpy and unnatural when she approaches that even Jennifer detects something wrong. She muses over the men's odd behavior in a sung soliloquy, "What's Going On Here?"

Her reverie is interrupted by the arrival of Julio, the only Mexican among the miners. He has rushed into town with his month's sack of laundry only to find that the Indian who comes at odd intervals to collect the camp washing and carry it back to San Francisco has just departed. Jennifer offers to do Julio's things herself, and the young Mexican lingers for a while talking to her.

An advertisement from *The New York Times*, run some weeks before the opening, which was postponed to Nov. 12 and took place at the Shubert Theatre.

In the course of their conversation, Jennifer impresses Julio as the first American who has ever shown him real sympathy, and, almost against his will, he is impelled to tell her his secret dream. Though he is young now, and illiterate, and an outcast from the camp, he plans to work hard and save his earnings until he can found his own splendid *rancho* on the California coast, where he will install his large family from Mexico and they will all learn to read and live like kings of the earth. Julio is overwhelmed by the enthusiasm with which Jennifer greets all this, and he expresses his gratitude—along with the first tentative stirrings of a deeper emotion—in the show's outstanding lyric, "I Talk to the Trees" (see p. 94).

After Julio and Jennifer drift away, several of the miners gather to continue their eternal discussion of the woman shortage. To take their minds off the prob-lem for a bit, one of them hauls out his guitar and sings the campfire ballad "They Call the Wind Maria" (see p. 98).

The following scene takes place two months later. A delegation of miners has come to Ben's cabin to warn him that the situation with Jennifer has become critical and that they cannot answer for the consequences if she continues to gallivant freely around the camp.

That evening, Ben informs Jennifer that she will be going east to school on the next stagecoach. He has always wanted this, he explains, because it will turn her into a lady, like her mother Elisa. He goes on to reminisce about his dead wife, whose extraordinary graces and accomplishments he recalls in the song "I Still See Elisa" (see p. 102).

Jennifer resists the idea on the pretext that Ben will not be able to get along without her, but her real reason

Jacob Woodling and his two wives come to Rumson Creek: Josh Wheeler (Jacob), Jan Sherwood (Sarah), and Marijane Maricle (Elizabeth). [PHOTO GEORGE KARGER]

WESTERN UNION

WESTERN UNION

WESTERN UNION

WESTERN UNION

WESTERN UNION

WESTERN UNION

NPD065 PD

LB BOSTON MASS OCT 10 246P

SAM ZOLOTOW

NEW YORK TIMES NYK

AFTER COMPLETING THREE HEALTHY WEEKS IN PHILADELPHIA WITH A TOTAL
GROSS OF $115,300, PAINT YOUR WAGON OPENED A THREE WEEK SESSION IN
BOSTON TUESDAY NIGHT AND RECEIVED A TREMENDOUSLY EXCITED PRESS RECEP-
TION. ELLIOT NORTON POST CALLED IT A HIT, SAID "THE SHOW" IS A
MASTERFUL MUSICAL PLAY: BIG, BRIGHT, SWIFT AND TURBULENT, A
SHOUTING, LAUGHING, ROMPING SONG-AND-DANCE SHOW WHICH FILLS
THE THEATRE WITH MELODY AND MERRIMENT. ALAN JAY LERNER IS WRITING AT
THE TOP OF HIS FORM HERE. FREDERICK LOEWE HAS SET HIS WORDS TO MUSIC
THAT BUBBLES UP OUT OF THE LIBRETTO, A GREAT BAG OF SONGS, PLAYED AND
SUNG BEAUTIFULLY. THE DANCES OF AGNES DE MILLE DAZZLE THE EYE AND
DECK OUT THE STATE IN MOVING SPLENDOR," ELINOR HUGHES IN HERALD SAYS:
"A REAL MUSICAL BONANZA, MORE TANGIBLE THAN THE GOLD STRIKES
PURSUED BY ITS PRINCIPAL CHARACTERS. MR. LOEWE'S MUSIC IS RICH,

NPD065/2 BOSTON MASS

RHYTHMIC AND TUNEFUL. THERE IS SO MUCH THAT'S GOOD ABOUT PLAY
THAT ITS HARD TO KNOW WHERE TO START, OR STOP FOR THAT MATTER, IN
EXTOLLING ITS MERITS. AMONG THE SUBSTANTIAL ASSETS IS JAMES
BARTON, A FINE ACTOR, GOOD DANCER AND ALL AROUND BOOSTER FOR EVERY
SCENE IN WHICH HE APPEARS." PEGGY DOYLE IN AMERICAN SAYS SHOW
"SEEMS A CERTAINTY TO STRIKE GOLD ON BROADWAY. ITS GREATEST ASSET
IS VETERAN TROUPER JAMES BARTON WHO SINGS DANCES AND ROMANCES AND
EXCELS IN ALL DEPARTMENTS." THANKS AND BEST.

WOLFE.

320P.

Wolfe Kaufman, the show's press agent, wires good news from Boston to the
theater desk of *The New York Times*. [COURTESY OF THE NEW YORK TIMES.]

comes out a moment later when Ben leaves her alone in the cabin and she sings of her growing, impatient love for Julio in "How Can I Wait?" (see p. 105). Her feelings for him have become so intense in the past months that the prospect of going away to school strikes Jennifer as a tragedy.

The following scene takes us to a hillside near Rumson, where a Mormon family traveling to the mines has set up camp. The family consists of Jacob Woodling, his two wives, Sarah and Elizabeth, and Sarah's infant child. We learn that Sarah, the first and the shrewder of the two wives, is exploiting and dominating Elizabeth and that the resulting tension is beginning to tell on Jacob.

Next morning the Woodlings arrive at Dutchie's saloon in Rumson, where Ben is sitting as judge in a frontier trial. The defendant is found guilty of petty theft and sentenced to hang. After that, the crowd turns its attention to the curious new arrivals. When Jacob states his intention to settle and stake a claim on Rumson Creek, the idea is greeted with general approval, though some of the miners grumble about the unfairness of anyone's having two wives where no one else has any. Ben, in his role as mayor, proposes that Woodling be allowed to settle on condition that he put up one wife at public auction, a proposal over which Elizabeth is particularly enthusiastic and which Jacob finally accepts.

In the auction that follows, Ben himself is the highest bidder for Elizabeth. Jennifer arrives in the midst of the proceedings to find her father prancing about in a state of high excitement, preparing for his "wedding." Shocked beyond words, Jennifer rushes away from the scene.

Late that evening, she bursts into Julio's cabin to tell him what she has seen and to announce her decision to take the stagecoach east the following day. This will be their last time together for many months, and they take the fleeting opportunity to assure one another of their undying love—Jennifer pleading with Julio to wait for her return and he swearing again and again that he will be there to meet her when she comes back.

The next day, the whole town is out to meet the stagecoach, coming from San Francisco and transporting the celebrated Cherry Jourdel with her company of fandango girls. There is a hilarious welcoming party when the girls finally appear, with the miners expressing their unbounded joy in the rousing strains of "There's a Coach Comin' In," and in the confusion Jennifer slips away on her eastbound journey almost unnoticed.

Act Two opens at Jake's Palace in Rumson on an October evening a year later. The interior decoration of the music hall is evidence that Rumson Creek has reached its apex as a wide-open, prosperous mining town. Some of the miners are dancing gaily with the fandango dancers. Others are involved in a high-stakes poker game run by a professional shark called Ray Janney, who, besides regularly cleaning the men of their earnings, has added to his unpopularity by taking a fancy to Ben's wife, Elizabeth.

The girls arrive at Rumson Creek. In the foreground, Joan Djorup and Robert Penn (Jake). [PHOTO GEORGE KARGER]

"Wonderful Theatre... a Musical Jamboree!"
—ATKINSON, TIMES

But, despite the general air of prosperity, the heyday of Rumson is already passing. As the evening wears on, one miner after another drifts into the bar to announce that he is moving along in the next day or two. One of them has become hypnotized by the legend of a lake of gold in the north, from which no man has ever returned alive. He wants to try his luck at finding it, and as he has no guide he approaches Julio, who at first refuses to go, true to his promise to Jennifer. But as more reports come in that the Rumson vein will soon give out and that the winter is likely to be a fierce one, Julio's resolve begins to grow shaky. Musically, he reflects on the awful prospect of "Another Autumn" (see p. 110) in the deserted mining camp, with its coldness and isolation. He changes his mind and agrees to go off in search of the golden lake.

The following scene takes place in Ben Rumson's cabin two months later. The Rumson vein has completely run out and, in just the abrupt way they came, almost all the miners have pulled up stakes and left. Elizabeth is alone in the cabin when Jennifer suddenly appears, unannounced and enormously changed by her experience at school, a genuine lady now, as her father hoped she would become. She announces that she has returned to marry Julio.

Her father enters a few minutes later, looking tired and depressed. As they talk, she learns of the failure of the lode and of the departure of the miners—including Julio. Ben himself is planning to move on too, as he explains in the song "Wand'rin' Star" (see p. 113).

Unable to believe that Julio has gone back on his promise, Jennifer sets out on a frantic search for him. When one of the fandango girls corroborates Ben's story, Jennifer, on the verge of tears, sings "I Talk to the Trees" one more time, as though it might bring Julio back to her.

A short while later, the few miners remaining in town gather for a last drink at Jake's Palace. The gambler Janney, who is the only one to have saved any of his money in the general catastrophe, offers to buy Elizabeth from Ben, just as Ben originally bought her from Jacob. Ben turns the proposition down self-righteously, until the price is raised from $1,000 to $3,000—at which point he accepts. A moment after the deal is concluded and the money is paid over, a man rushes in to say that Elizabeth has run off with another miner.

After this interlude, a general depression settles over the crowd. But it dissolves in an instant when a stranger enters the bar to announce that a new gold strike has been made only forty miles away!

In the ensuing excitement, the miners tumble over one another in their hurry to get off and stake their claims. In a matter of minutes, they are all gone—all but Ben. At the very last moment he realizes that he cannot possibly leave: Rumson is his town.

The final scene takes place in Rumson Square the following spring. Rumson has become a ghost town, with only six of its four thousand inhabitants still remaining. Ben and Jacob are still holding on, resolved somehow to bring the town back to prosperity. As the two men stand discussing their plans in the otherwise deserted square, Julio enters, tired and defeated-looking. Without much hope, he inquires after Jennifer.

At the same instant, Jennifer appears in the doorway of the old store building and catches sight of Julio. They come to one another and embrace, while offstage a chorus of miners sings "I'm on My Way" in the same key of unquenchable optimism as at the opening.

I'm on My Way

Copyright © 1951 by Alan Jay Lerner and Frederick Loewe
Chappell & Co., Inc., New York, N.Y., Publisher and Owner of allied rights

I Talk to the Trees

Copyright © 1951 by Alan Jay Lerner and Frederick Loewe
Chappell & Co., Inc., New York, N.Y., Publisher and Owner of allied rights

They Call the Wind Maria

1. A - way out here they got a name for rain, and wind, and fi - re. The
(2. Be-) fore I knew Ma - ri - a's name And heard her wail and whin - in'. I
(3. Out) here they got a name for rain, For wind and fi - re on - ly. But

Copyright © 1951 by Alan Jay Lerner and Frederick Loewe
Chappell & Co., Inc., New York, N.Y., Publisher and Owner of allied rights

I Still See Elisa

Copyright © 1951 by Alan Jay Lerner and Frederick Loewe
Chappell & Co., Inc., New York, N.Y., Publisher and Owner of allied rights

How Can I Wait?

Copyright © 1951 (unpub.) and 1952 by Alan Jay Lerner and Frederick Loewe
Chappell & Co., Inc., New York, N.Y., Publisher and Owner of allied rights

Another Autumn

Copyright © 1951 by Alan Jay Lerner and Frederick Loewe
Chappell & Co., Inc., New York, N.Y., Publisher and Owner of allied rights

Wand'rin' Star

Copyright © 1951 by Alan Jay Lerner and Frederick Loewe
Chappell & Co., Inc., New York, N.Y., Publisher and Owner of allied rights

Stand-in' still's a curse; To set-tle down can drive you mad, But mov-in' on is worse.

I was born under a wand' - rin'

star. When I learned to talk, the word they taught me was "good-bye."

That and "Where's my hat" are all I need un-til I die. Ach-in' for to stop and al-ways

My Fair Lady

OPENED MARCH 15, 1956, AT THE MARK HELLINGER THEATRE—2,717 PERFORMANCES

Book and Lyrics by ALAN JAY LERNER ❧ *Music by* FREDERICK LOEWE

PRODUCED BY HERMAN LEVIN

PRODUCTION STAGED BY MOSS HART

CHOREOGRAPHY AND MUSICAL NUMBERS BY HANYA HOLM

PRODUCTION DESIGNED BY OLIVER SMITH

COSTUMES DESIGNED BY CECIL BEATON

MUSICAL ARRANGEMENTS BY ROBERT RUSSELL BENNETT AND PHILIP J. LANG

LIGHTING BY FEDER

DANCE MUSIC ARRANGED BY TRUDE RITTMAN

MUSICAL DIRECTOR: FRANZ ALLERS

ADAPTED FROM BERNARD SHAW'S *Pygmalion*

PRODUCED ON THE SCREEN BY GABRIEL PASCAL

ORIGINAL CAST

[IN ORDER OF APPEARANCE]

BUSKERS	IMELDA DE MARTIN, CARL JEFFREY, JOE ROCCO
MRS. EYNSFORD-HILL	VIOLA ROACHE
ELIZA DOOLITTLE	JULIE ANDREWS
FREDDY EYNSFORD-HILL	JOHN MICHAEL KING
COLONEL PICKERING	ROBERT COOTE
A BYSTANDER	LEO BRITT
HENRY HIGGINS	REX HARRISON
SELSEY MAN	GORDON DILWORTH
HOXTON MAN	DAVID THOMAS
ANOTHER BYSTANDER	ROD McLENNAN
FIRST COCKNEY	REID SHELTON
SECOND COCKNEY	GLENN KEZER
THIRD COCKNEY	JAMES MORRIS
FOURTH COCKNEY	HERB SURFACE
BARTENDER	DAVID THOMAS
HARRY	GORDON DILWORTH
JAMIE	ROD McLENNAN
ALFRED P. DOOLITTLE	STANLEY HOLLOWAY
MRS. PEARCE	PHILIPPA BEVANS
MRS. HOPKINS	OLIVE REEVES-SMITH
BUTLER	REID SHELTON
SERVANTS	ROSEMARY GAINES, COLLEEN O'CONNOR, MURIEL SHAW, GLORIA VAN DORPE, GLENN KEZER
MRS. HIGGINS	CATHLEEN NESBITT
CHAUFFEUR	BARTON MUMAW
FOOTMEN	GORDON EWING, WILLIAM KRACH
LORD BOXINGTON	GORDON DILWORTH
LADY BOXINGTON	OLIVE REEVES-SMITH
CONSTABLE	BARTON MUMAW
FLOWER GIRL	CATHY CONKLIN
ZOLTAN KARPATHY	CHRISTOPHER HEWETT
FLUNKEY	PAUL BROWN
QUEEN OF TRANSYLVANIA	MARIBEL HAMMER
AMBASSADOR	ROD McLENNAN
BARTENDER	PAUL BROWN
MRS. HIGGINS' MAID	JUDITH WILLIAMS

My Fair Lady

THERE CAN BE NO SERIOUS DOUBT THAT *My Fair Lady* enlarged and extended the tradition of the American musical theater, solved old problems and suggested new ones, as no single show but *Oklahoma* had done before. It was the culminating point in its authors' fifteen-year development, and it contained in highly refined and sophisticated form many of the objectives toward which the two men had been working all that time. Nothing quite like it had ever appeared before—even from Lerner and Loewe. And it was unlikely that any important musical play could appear in the foreseeable future that did not bear the mark of its influence.

It enjoyed an immediate and unprecedented success. Indeed, so rapidly did *My Fair Lady* soar to the summit of popularity, so brilliant was the dazzle of glamor that surrounded it from the very start, that its very success threatened partly to obscure the lasting artistic achievement that lay behind it all.

That achievement was built, as all the Lerner and Loewe collaborations have been, on long years of work

and a series of fundamental decisions about the proper approach to the material in hand, sometimes empirical, more often based on central principles evolved over the years the authors had worked together.

The first of these decisions was, of course, the choice of Bernard Shaw's *Pygmalion* as a source for adaptation. The Shaw play had been considered before by Cole Porter, Rodgers and Hammerstein, and others and had been discarded. Lerner and Loewe themselves had had a crack at it in 1952 and had given the project up. When they returned to it in 1954, the difficulties that had stymied them two years earlier remained unsolved.

The major themes of the play were both more complex and "heavier" than musical comedy had previously been thought capable of bearing. First, there was the Greek myth of the artist's endowing his material with such a quantity of genius and love that it takes on breathing, passionate life. Second, there was Shaw's contention that class distinctions, the curse of modern society, were entirely a matter of externals, mainly accent and vocabulary, and would crumble away when every citizen was given a fair and equal chance to master his native tongue.

Complicating the problem of theme was that of style. Shaw's rapid, complex, and lengthy dialectic was the very antithesis of typical musical-comedy dialogue. Another problem was posed by the original setting—a single, purposely drab interior.

Further, the plot not only contained no overt romantic sentiment but also depended absolutely on the misogyny of the leading male character. Nor, for that matter, was either of the principals exactly promising as Broadway musical material: Henry Higgins, a spoiled, cranky dryasdust, a woman hater, and a fanatic student of phonetics; and Eliza Doolittle, a shrill, squalid, unattractive flower girl, foulmouthed and vulgarly aggressive.

There was, of course, an overwhelming temptation simply to evade most of the difficulties. One might retain only the sketchiest elements of Shaw's plot and dialogue. The setting could be completely transformed along any one of a number of exotic lines. The basic structure might be chucked and the leading ideas ignored. But each of these temptations was resisted. In an article written after *My Fair Lady* opened, Lerner contended that it was only by sticking with the basic dynamic of the original play that any success at all was achieved. Whatever attempt he might have made to force *Pygmalion* into some other mold would have resulted inevitably in an artistic as well as a commercial failure.

So the basic form of the play was honored and much of the original dialogue was retained. To bring the story out of Higgins' study, Lerner speculated on the action that must have taken place *between* Shaw's scenes and so was able to create episodes—like the scenes of Eliza Doolittle in the slums of London and the famous "port-wine scene" before the ball—which filled out but did not interrupt the flow of the original story.

The question of dialectic subtlety and "talkiness" was as much a musical problem as a dramatic one. It became clear as work on the show progressed that the songs given to Professor Higgins—as a result both of his character and of the intellectual burden they would have to bear—had to be entirely conversational, that they should give the impression of being "spoken" rather than sung. This consideration carried with it one advantage: the role could be played by a dramatic actor, one whose singing voice need not meet the conventional requirements of the musical stage but who would lend dramatic force to the whole production. But it also forced on the authors the task of producing a new sort of song that precisely reproduced the rhythms of witty, cultivated speech while still being full of melody and not falling into the dreary flatness of recitative.

More than in any of their earlier shows, the Lerner-Loewe insistence on every single song's deriving directly from character became crucial. The construction of Shaw's play was so delicately balanced that any song which seemed to have been arbitrarily imposed would surely have shattered the mood of the whole.

An outstanding example of this last point was the

Road sign for eastbound traffic in Los Angeles, 1956.

Stanley Holloway (Alfred P. Doolittle), Julie Andrews (Eliza Doolittle), Rex Harrison
(Henry Higgins), and other decorative elements as Al Hirschfeld saw them.

apparent impossibility of including a specifically romantic tune sung by either of the major characters without violating the tone of the original model. Shaw had
carefully excluded anything of the sort from his play.
But, rigorous as they were, Lerner and Loewe recognized the utter futility of attempting to construct a
popular musical play without at least one point of ex-
plicit lyric sentiment. For months they worked to evolve
a lyric, romantic song that would suggest, as Shaw's
script had done, the developing attachment between
Eliza and Higgins without openly stating it. The entirely successful result of their labors was "I Could Have
Danced All Night" (see p. 143).

The preparation of the show went on over two years.
("Whatever we do, it *always* takes two years," Lerner
said later.) During that time, the tangled legal problems
that surrounded the rights to the show were settled
with Shaw's estate and a full complement of intensely
creative talents was assembled around the authors. Rex
Harrison and Julie Andrews took the leading roles. Each
of them worked closely with the authors on the final
versions of their own songs; at the same time, they were

working out their subtle, memorable characterizations
of Higgins and Eliza. Cecil Beaton turned his magic
hand to the costumes, and Moss Hart's genius and un-
stinting devotion in his capacity as director contributed
incalculably to the artistic distinction of the production.
Finally, *My Fair Lady* was ready to meet the public.

The show opened at the Mark Hellinger Theatre on
March 15, 1956. By the following morning, it was an
indisputable smash hit. It ran for more than six years
on Broadway. It broke records in, among other places,
London, Stockholm, Melbourne, Dallas, Winnipeg, and
Helsinki. The original-cast album has sold well over
four million copies. For years, tickets to *My Fair Lady*
stood as a synonym for the unattainable.

Critical reaction to the show was so immediate,
abundant, and repetitious in its enthusiasm that there
is little point in reproducing much of it here. One of
the show's admirers does stand out from the rest, however. James Thurber yielded to no man in his early
and vigorous and profoundly understanding devotion
to the show.

"I can still be heard proclaiming on street corners,"

he wrote in the summer of 1956, "that *My Fair Lady* has restored comedy to a position of dignity in the American theater.... By dignity I mean the high place attained only when the heart and mind are lifted, equally and at once, by the creative union of perception and grace...."

THE FIRST ENCOUNTER between Professor Henry Higgins, the brilliant, crotchety, middle-aged bachelor who is England's leading phoneticist, and Eliza Doolittle, the little cockney gutter sparrow, takes place near the Royal Opera House, Covent Garden, late on a cold March night. Eliza is selling her violets to the fashionable crowd spilling out of the theater. Higgins is out on his endless quest after new varieties of London's speech. He is both fascinated and appalled by Eliza's hideous accent, and it moves him to pronounce a diatribe on the subject: "Why Can't the English Teach Their Children How to Speak?"

In the course of the scene, Eliza approaches a handsome young aristrocrat named Freddy Eynsford-Hill, asking him to buy a bunch of flowers, but the young man takes no notice of her whatsoever. Just afterward, Higgins has a chance encounter with a certain Colonel Pickering of the Indian Army, who is, it turns out, a linguistic expert, too, and is now in London specifically to meet Higgins, on whom he was planning to call the next day. The two men are instantly drawn to one another, with the result that Higgins insists on Pickering's coming to stay with him at his Wimpole Street flat.

When the two friends have gone off in the wake of the opera crowd, Eliza joins a group of costermongers huddled together about a smudge pot. With them, she sings "Wouldn't It Be Loverly?" (see p. 132), the lyric expression of their longing for the very minimum in creature comforts.

Next on the scene is Eliza's father, Alfred Doolittle. The old reprobate has just been forcibly ejected from a Tottenham Court Road pub. But, still unaffected by the indigence, squalor, and apparent hopelessness of his situation, he outlines his optimistic if somewhat unorthodox philosophy of life in the rousing "With a Little Bit of Luck" (see p. 135).

The following scene takes place the morning after in Higgins' study, where he and Pickering are deeply immersed in scientific talk. They are interrupted by the unannounced arrival of Eliza. It appears that the Professor's angry speech the night before has made a deep impression on her, and she has gone to the trouble somehow to track him down. She has come, she says, to be instructed in the English language, so that she may transform herself into a "lidy."

Higgins turns her down flat. But Pickering is touched by the girl's problem and offers to pay for the lessons—if, that is, Higgins can succeed in doing what he always boasted he could do: to wit, metamorphose a guttersnipe into a paragon of verbal correctitude.

Higgins accepts the challenge. It is clear, though, that he feels nothing for Eliza as a person, regarding her merely as raw material for his experiment. Indeed, he is predisposed to be irritated with her for the mere fact of being a woman. He explains the causes of his deep-seated misogyny to Pickering in "I'm an Ordinary Man."

That afternoon, even before the first lesson, Higgins receives a visit from Eliza's father. Convinced that the scholar's interest in his daughter must be something other than scientific, Doolittle demands five pounds as hush money. Delighted with Doolittle's utter lack of scruples, Higgins pays him gladly.

Shortly after, the lessons begin. They go on and on for weeks. And Higgins runs them like a tyrant. He gives Eliza no rest and no encouragement. She must drill from morning till night: "The rain in Spain stays mainly in the plain" to wrench her hideous *aiiii* sounds into ladylike *ays* and "In Hertford, Hereford, and Hampshire hurricanes hardly happen" to restore her nonexistent aitches.

But still there is no hint of progress. Eliza loses her courage and Higgins loses his temper. Even Pickering's patience wears thin. But the lessons go on. In her anger and sense of futility, Eliza creates a set of sadistic fantasies involving her professor: Higgins broke, Higgins ill or drowning, Higgins about to be hanged, and all with her standing by, not raising a finger to help. She sings "Just You Wait," but it is all to no avail. The lessons continue remorselessly, and still with no sign of progress.

Until suddenly, miraculously, Higgins cries out: "She's got it!" And she does: the rine no longer falls in Spine; nor do urricanes appen in Artford. All together, Higgins, Pickering, and Eliza proclaim their first victory in the very—properly pronounced—words of the devilish exercise, "The Rain in Spain" (see p. 139). Higgins' excitement is so intense that he falls out of

Eliza (Julie Andrews) invades the library of Professor Higgins (Rex Harrison) as Colonel Pickering (Robert Coote) watches quizzically. [PHOTO FRIEDMAN–ABELES]

character to the point of guiding Eliza through a few awkward, hilarious waltz steps. And in the flush of his first success he resolves to put Eliza to a preliminary test. He will introduce her to his mother's snobbish guests at the Ascot Race Meeting the following week.

After Higgins and Pickering have retired, Eliza expresses her own towering exaltation in the song "I Could Have Danced All Night" (see p. 143), whirling about the deserted study in mock continuation of her brief victory waltz with Higgins. Although her mood is not precisely romantic, it is clear enough that her sense of triumph is intimately tied up with a new feeling for Higgins.

A week later Colonel Pickering is found conferring with Higgins' mother in her box at Ascot. Both of them are apprehensive about the forthcoming experiment, though their misgivings are calmed a little when Higgins and Eliza make their appearance, she strikingly pretty in her new gown and hairdo, he absolutely unintimidated by the brilliant setting and the bored, snobbish, hypercritical company assembling there.

For a while, Eliza lives up to all his expectations. Instructed to restrict her conversation to two subjects, the weather and everyone's health, she says her little set pieces flawlessly. The illusion is shattered only when her enthusiasm for the horse she is backing impels her to indulge in a bout of violently unladylike cheering: "Come on, Dover!!! Move your bloomin' arse!!!"

There is, however, one entirely positive result of the Ascot excursion. Mrs. Higgins' party includes the young Freddy Eynsford-Hill, who falls hopelessly in love with the new Eliza on sight and remains in that condition despite her final gaffe. Later that day he arrives in Wimpole Street, bearing flowers. Denied entry to Higgins' house by a maid, he pours out his unashamed, uncontrollable feelings beneath Eliza's window in the song "On the Street Where You Live" (see p. 148).

Six weeks later, Higgins is found once more in his study, now finally prepared for the last crucial test. This evening he will present Eliza at a full-dress Embassy Ball. As usual, Pickering is full of trepidation, but Higgins is outwardly calm, even cocky. When Eliza appears in the doorway, a vision in her spectacular ball gown, he is moved to rare praise: "Not bad. Not bad at all."

Higgins, Eliza, and Pickering proceed to the ball. Eliza's stately entrance is the object of universal admiration, and soon everyone there is busily speculating on her identity. Both Higgins and Pickering are relieved by their early success, though they remain aware that Eliza has not yet passed the crucial test.

Shortly after the ball begins, Higgins spots Professor Karpathy, a phonetics expert of European reputation and a man whose overweening self-confidence matches, if it does not exceed, Higgins' own. To top all, he is Higgins' bitterest rival. It is obvious that the conclusive test will be Eliza's ability to take in Karpathy, who, at the height of the ball, invites her to dance.

The trick succeeds beyond anyone's wildest dreams. Karpathy not only is taken but also goes so far as to declare that Eliza's English is too pure for any native Englishman. She must be a foreigner—a Hungarian princess.

The second act opens back in Wimpole Street at three in the morning following the ball. Pickering and Higgins have given themselves over to an orgy of self-congratulation, with Pickering repeating over and over again to his friend, "You did it! You did it!" Neither of the men seems to take any account of Eliza's personal accomplishment in the matter. But, along with her English lessons, Eliza has absorbed the sophistication and the courage to see the unfairness of this, and she blows up. She demands recognition. And she asks Higgins what plans he has made for her future.

The Professor is not so much affronted as astonished; it is as though a statue had spoken from its niche. Eliza quickly recognizes that she can make no headway against his obtuseness, that he has never considered her as a human being and is not willing to now, and that he has made no plans for her future and has always imagined that he could drop her when his experiment was finished. Infuriated and frustrated, she storms out of the house.

In the street outside the house, she encounters Freddy, still keeping his lonely vigil. When he hastens to declare his love for her, Eliza turns on him, transferring to him her fury at Higgins, blistering the poor infatuated boy with the challenge that he not waste his time speaking of love but—"Show Me" (see p. 154).

Through the rest of the night, Eliza aimlessly walks the streets of the town, returning to most of her old haunts. In one of them she runs into her father, drunk as a lord and dressed, oddly enough, for a fashionable wedding. Sadly he explains that through a wild fluke he has recently become wealthy beyond his hopes or desires and that, in the wake of prosperity and respecta-

Rod McLennan (Jamie), Stanley Holloway (Alfred), and Gordon Dilworth (Harry) sing "With a Little Bit of Luck." [PHOTO FRIEDMAN–ABELES]

Cecil Beaton's costume sketches for an anonymous spectator *(left)* and for Mrs. Higgins *(right)* as they appear in the Ascot scene designed by Oliver Smith *(below)*.

Mrs. Eynsford-Hill (Viola Roache), Lord Boxington (Gordon Dilworth), Freddy Eynsford-Hill (John Michael King), Eliza (Julie Andrews), Lady Boxington (Olive Reeves-Smith), and Mrs. Higgins (Cathleen Nesbitt) watch the horses (or each other) at Ascot. [PHOTO FRIEDMAN–ABELES]

Cecil Beaton's sketches for two of the costumes of the guests at the ball and Oliver Smith's design for the ball scene.

At the embassy ball, Professor Zoltan Karpathy (Christopher Hewett) arrives at the conclusion that Eliza Doolittle (Julie Andrews, dancing with Rex Harrison) must be a Hungarian princess. [PHOTO FRIEDMAN–ABELES]

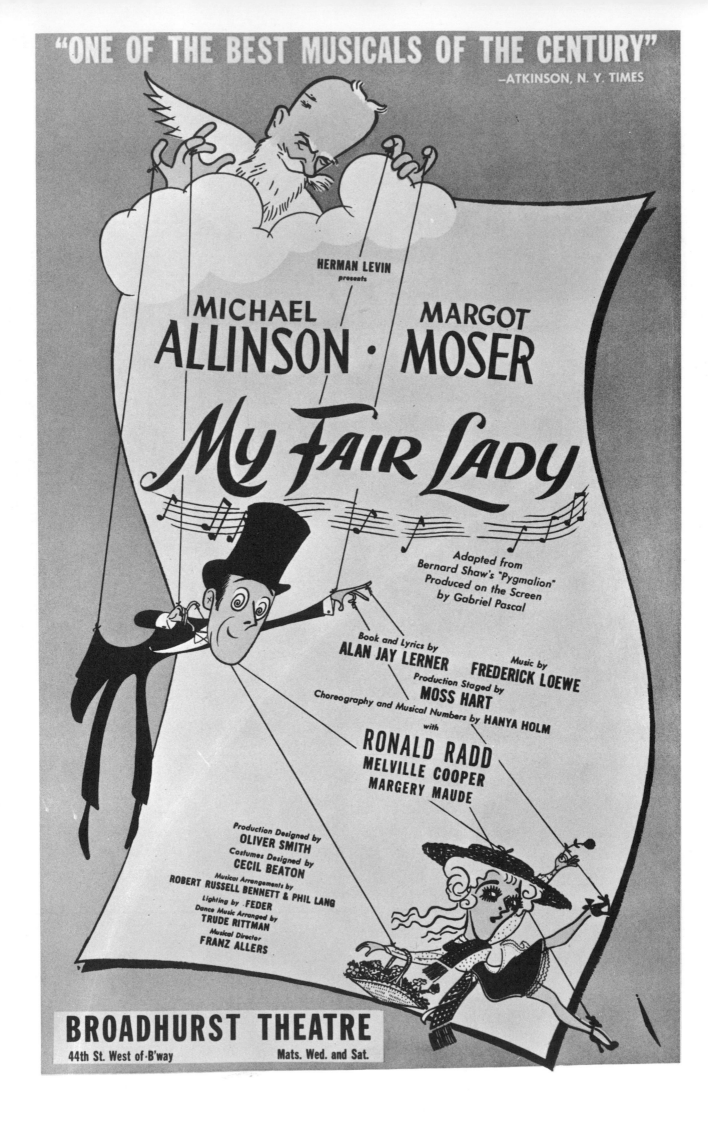

bility, Eliza's mother is forcing him to make an honest woman of her at last. Today is the day. Doolittle gives his daughter an exuberant account of the prenuptial celebrations in the song "Get Me to the Church on Time" (see p. 158).

Meanwhile, Higgins has awakened to the fact that Eliza has really left him and has discovered, very much to his surprise, that he is hurt, angry, and distraught over the fact. Fuming about his flat, he racks his brain for some device for forcing her to come back to him, though without ever consciously admitting the affection he feels for her, and, by an odd quirk, making of her defection one final confirmation of his own misogyny.

Shortly after this scene, Eliza is found in the drawing room of Higgins' mother, where she has come for advice and comfort, as to the only port in a storm. But before Mrs. Higgins can say a word to the girl, the Professor himself bursts in. A violent argument breaks out, through which Mrs. Higgins does what she can to keep some order, but without much success. Higgins accuses Eliza of heartlessness, and she accuses him of the same thing.

There appears to be no chance of an accommodation. Higgins boasts that he can get on perfectly well without Eliza. Suddenly stirred to independence, Eliza replies that almost anything she wants to do she can do "Without You." Including marrying Freddy, she announces, which is precisely what she proposes to do. On this note she once more storms out of Higgins' presence.

It is only a moment after her departure that Higgins finally wakes up to the fact that Eliza has become an entirely independent and admirable human being. And she has proved this to him only by the act of openly facing up to him in her last speech, in her own words, and on her own initiative.

Higgins makes his way home, depressed by his realization that now he really will have a terribly difficult time getting on without Eliza, a fact that he admits to himself in the form of a crucial concession: "I've Grown Accustomed to Her Face" (see p. 162).

Back in Wimpole Street, he sinks dejectedly into his chair, prepared to face a bleak, lonely future. But just then—a moment before the final curtain falls—a figure emerges from the shadowy corner of the room, and Higgins recognizes Eliza. He leans back with a long, contented sigh and speaks softly: "Eliza? Where the devil are my slippers?"

As *My Fair Lady* ran on for years and years, new faces appeared in the cast. When this poster appeared, Michael Allinson was Henry Higgins, Margot Moser was Eliza, Ronald Radd was Freddy, Melville Cooper was Mr. Doolittle, and Margery Maude was Mrs. Higgins.

Wouldn't It Be Loverly?

Copyright © 1956 by Alan Jay Lerner and Frederick Loewe.
Chappell & Co., Inc., New York, N.Y., Publisher and Owner of allied rights.

With a Little Bit of Luck

Copyright © 1956 by Alan Jay Lerner and Frederick Loewe.
Chappell & Co., Inc., New York, N.Y., Publisher and Owner of allied rights.

The Rain in Spain

Copyright © 1956 by Alan Jay Lerner and Frederick Loewe
Chappell & Co., Inc., New York, N.Y., Publisher and Owner of allied rights

I Could
Have Danced All Night

Copyright © 1956 by Alan Jay Lerner and Frederick Loewe.
Chappell & Co., Inc., New York, N.Y., Publisher and Owner of allied rights.

On the Street Where You Live

Copyright © 1956 by Alan Jay Lerner and Frederick Loewe.
Chappell & Co., Inc., New York, N.Y., Publisher and Owner of allied rights.

Just to know_____ some-how you are near!_____

The o - ver pow-er-ing feel - ing_____

That an - y se-cond you may sud-den-ly ap - pear!_____

Peo-ple stop and stare,_____ they don't both - er me;_____

Show Me

Copyright © 1956 by Alan Jay Lerner and Frederick Loewe.
Chappell & Co., Inc., New York, N.Y., Publisher and Owner of allied rights.

Get Me to the Church on Time

Copyright © 1956 by Alan Jay Lerner and Frederick Loewe.
Chappell & Co., Inc., New York, N.Y., Publisher and Owner of allied rights.

I've Grown Accustomed to Her Face

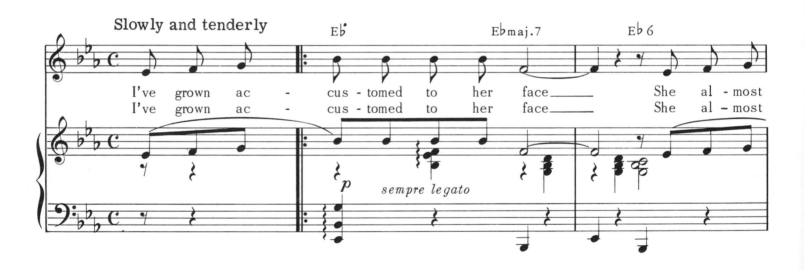

I've grown ac - cus - tomed to her face____ She al - most
I've grown ac - cus - tomed to her face____ She al - most

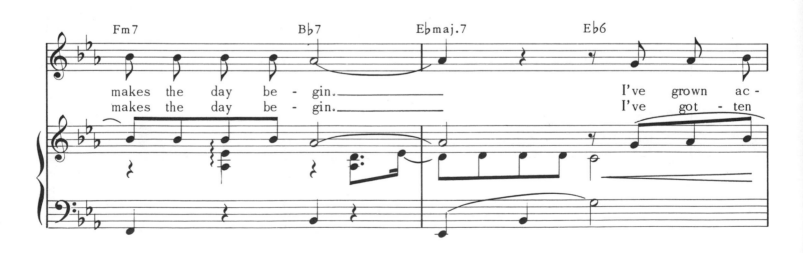

makes the day be - gin._____ I've grown ac -
makes the day be - gin._____ I've got - ten

Copyright © 1956 by Alan Jay Lerner and Frederick Loewe.
Chappell & Co., Inc., New York, N.Y., Publisher and Owner of allied rights.

Gigi

[BASED ON THE NOVEL BY COLETTE]

Screenplay and Lyrics by ALAN JAY LERNER ❈ *Music by* FREDERICK LOEWE

PRESENTED BY M-G-M AND PRODUCED BY ARTHUR FREED
DIRECTED BY VINCENTE MINNELLI
MUSIC SUPERVISED AND CONDUCTED BY ANDRÉ PREVIN
ORCHESTRATIONS BY CONRAD SALINGER
ART DIRECTORS: WILLIAM A. HORNING AND PRESTON AMES
COSTUMES, SCENERY AND PRODUCTION DESIGNED BY CECIL BEATON

CAST

GIGI	LESLIE CARON
HONORE LACHAILLE	MAURICE CHEVALIER
GASTON LACHAILLE	LOUIS JOURDAN
MME. ALVAREZ	HERMIONE GINGOLD
LIANE D'EXELMANS	EVA GABOR
SANDOMIR	JACQUES BERGERAC
AUNT ALICIA	ISABEL JEANS
MANUEL	JOHN ABBOTT

Gigi

FREDERICK LOEWE ONCE MADE A SOLEMN VOW, which he managed to stick to for many years: never, ever, he promised himself, would he write the score for a Hollywood film. It was only the temptation to do *Gigi* that, in 1957, finally defeated him. His partner was, of course, an old movie hand, having written two original screenplays for M-G-M, *Royal Wedding* and the brilliant *American in Paris,* as well as the screen adaptations of *Brigadoon* and *My Fair Lady.*

The job of talking Loewe out of his resolve fell to Lerner and Arthur Freed, the producer with whom Lerner had done all his previous film work. Two considerations finally won Loewe over. First was Lerner's absolute trust in Freed as a producer and second was the absorbing musical problem offered by the Colette story that Lerner proposed to adapt: the challenge to create a musical setting that would be typically "Parisian" without at the same time seeming merely antique.

Here again was the old question of creating a coherent musical idiom out of familiar traditional forms, much as it had been posed before by *Brigadoon* and *Paint Your Wagon.* In the present case, the solution would be still harder to find, if only because the tradition was even more widely known and closer to the composer's own background. What could he write that would be Parisian and not sound like Offenbach? Nevertheless, Loewe agreed to go ahead.

The technique of collaboration was the one they had developed in their early days of working together and have stuck to ever since. It begins with a long series of general conversations between the two authors—weeks of them. (In the case of *My Fair Lady* they devoted literally months to this stage in the process.) The object of these sessions is to feel their way into the story, to seek out problems and difficulties, to suggest and reject lines of attack to various scenes and musical situations.

Only very gradually do they move from general considerations to particular isolated points. No writing is done. Both men have often stated that this preliminary, intentionally relaxed and unspecific work is a key factor in the success of all their productions.

As the show begins to emerge in final form, more and more collaborators are brought into these conferences—producers, directors, actors, choreographers, designers, and publicity men. With *Gigi* these latter stages were more feverish, if that is possible, than were those for any of Lerner's and Loewe's▪ theatrical ventures. Though the authors were spared the agonies of opening in New Haven, the bewildering technical demands of Hollywood—which Loewe still regarded with a somewhat suspicious eye—provided all the last-minute complications the authors needed to make them feel at home.

Along the way, of course, they had had to face as many artistic problems as with any of their plays. Lerner's first preoccupation was with setting. The magnificent Colette novella he was adapting was set firmly in two drawing rooms. It almost cried out for being adapted to the conventional proscenium stage (as indeed it had been by Anita Loos in 1952). Even if Lerner had been writing for the musical stage, that option would not have been available to him; and for the film, the action of the story had to be radically enlarged without disrupting the extremely tight story line. As in *My Fair Lady*, a good deal of tough, witty, even anti-romantic writing had to be accommodated by both the scenarist and the composer.

An early decision was made to set the city of Paris at the center of the stage, to make of it something like an extra—even the dominating—character in the story. After all, a large part of the impact of Colette's story derived from the glittering life of the demimonde, with all its brilliance and its intrinsic shallowness—a life that she could suggest to her readers by the merest touches. The film, then, would directly present the glamor of Maxim's and the Bois, Trouville, the sidewalk cafés, and the Palais de Glace.

Cecil Beaton's sets and costumes formed an invaluable contribution to this end, as did Vincente Minnelli's direction. The proof that they all escaped the many temptations to banality that inevitably arose is provided by the Oscars awarded *Gigi* for best film of the year, musical score, song ("Gigi"), screenplay, costumes, art direction, color photography, director and editor.

To enlarge the action, the character of Honoré La-

chaille, the hero's roué uncle, was expanded and the role was entrusted to Maurice Chevalier. Loewe worked and reworked his musical material, eliminating much more than was ever used, until his critical ear was satisfied that he had achieved a setting that was indubitably French but without any staling derivativeness. To make certainty doubly sure, the Parisian flavor of the enterprise was enhanced by assigning the juvenile leads to Louis Jourdan and Leslie Caron, both of whom turned in much-praised performances, as did Hermione Gingold and Eva Gabor in supporting roles.

The critical response to the film when it opened at the Royale Theatre in New York was almost universally enthusiastic. The only dissenters based their criticism on the contention that *Gigi* closely resembled *My Fair Lady* in tone and style. The authors, like their public, tended to accept this criticism as disguised praise. And at the 1958 Academy Awards *Gigi* won more Oscars than any other picture in history.

As *The New York Times* put it, *Gigi* looked very much as though it had established itself as "the *Fair Lady* of filmdom."

The action opens in the Bois de Boulogne on a sunny afternoon around the turn of the century. Honoré Lachaille, a wealthy and charming, if somewhat superannuated, roué is seated on a park bench, from which he commands a view of the passing scene, the most striking features in which are, of course, feminine. His attention falls on a group of schoolgirls playing nearby, and he waxes eloquent over their particular attractions in the song "Thank Heaven for Little Girls" (see p. 178).

One of the children—Gigi—suddenly detaches herself from the group and rushes off. A few minutes later she arrives at her apartment door to find her grandmother perturbed by the fact that Gigi is already late for a luncheon date with her Aunt Alicia.

Meantime, Honoré has left the park and made his way to the fantastically chic home of his nephew Gaston. Gaston's father is an immensely wealthy sugar refiner, and his mother is one of the most brilliant of Paris hostesses. The life of the house is the very epitome of luxury and fashion, complete with priceless antiques and jewelry, stunning maids, and fawning tradesmen. Gaston is unutterably bored by the whole thing.

A few moments later, Honoré and Gaston are in-

On their way to a luncheon party, Honoré Lachaille (Maurice Chevalier) hymns the rich delights of Paris life, but his nephew Gaston (Louis Jourdan) repeatedly replies, "It's a bore!" [PHOTO M-G-M]

stalled in a carriage, bound for a fashionable luncheon party, and Honoré is, as usual, enthusing over the rich delights provided by Paris life—particularly the young lady he expects to meet at the party. His life is full of zest; but not so his nephew's. As the ride progresses, Honoré attempts to transmit some of his irrepressible joy in life to Gaston, but with little success, and the conversation develops into the dialogue song "It's a Bore."

Suddenly, unable to face the prospect of one more luncheon in society, Gaston jumps out of the carriage and hastens to the home of Mme. Alvarez, the only place in Paris, he has said, where he can enjoy himself. Mme.

Alvarez is Gigi's grandmother. She receives the young man cordially, settles him into "his" chair, and offers him a cup of her special camomile tea—after which he inquires about Gigi.

The scene shifts to the home of Aunt Alicia, where the old lady is awaiting Gigi's arrival while she dreams over her extraordinary career as a lady of fortune, when she numbered kings and sultans among her protectors— a career which she intends Gigi to follow in her turn and for which she is carefully training her in a series of weekly lessons in the arts and graces of the demi-monde.

Suddenly Gigi clatters into the room helter-skelter.

Cecil Beaton's photographic portrayal of Leslie Caron as Gigi and Isabel Jeans as Aunt Alicia.

have to take her seriously as he does the worldly women with whom he spends much of his time. On an impulse, he offers to take her along with him to the Ice Palace, where he is to meet his current mistress, Liane.

When they arrive, they find Liane waltzing on the ice in the arms of her skating instructor, Sandomir. While they wait, Gigi and Gaston carry on a lively discussion of the seamy side of Paris society, a subject in which Gigi takes a passionate interest. Among other things, she expresses her frank opinion of the notorious Mme. d'Exelmans—Liane herself—whom she finds "common." Finally, Sandomir escorts Liane to Gaston's table. During his conversation with Gigi, Gaston was observing Sandomir and Liane together; now that he is alone with Liane, he accuses her—not unjustly—of taking a rather too lively interest in the skating teacher.

The next scene takes place that evening at Maxim's,

Mr. Beaton's costume sketch for Miss Jeans.

First Aunt Alicia makes her repeat her entrance in a ladylike way. Then they settle down to their lesson in earnest, beginning with the proper method of eating ortolans—tiny game birds—bones and all. While Aunt Alicia performs the feat effortlessly, Gigi loudly crunches every bone. The session goes on to an examination of Aunt Alicia's imposing jewelry case, during which the aunt discusses the value of each stone and just what sort of admirer can be expected to provide one like it.

Gigi is on her way back to her Grandmama's house an hour or so later when she passes one pair of lovers after another in amorous—typically Parisian—poses. It is the normal landscape of the city, but it has recently begun to trouble Gigi. She expresses her feelings of puzzlement and concern in the song "I Don't Understand the Parisians."

Still deep in her quandary, Gigi encounters Gaston, with whom, it is clear on first sight, she gets along famously in a kidding, brother-and-sister way. They giggle and chatter together, and, of course, he does not

Liane (Eva Gabor) and Gaston (Louis Jourdan), the most brilliant guests at
Maxim's. [COURTESY CECIL BEATON]

where Gaston and Liane are the most brilliant and the
most talked-about couple in the restaurant. As usual,
Gaston is bored to distraction. But, beyond that, he is
disturbed by the fact that Liane is being even more
tender and solicitous than usual. He smells a rat—a rat
named Sandomir—and his suspicions of Liane take the
form of an obsessive internal monologue, "She Is Not
Thinking of Me" (see p. 182).

Gigi tries to get the attention of her elders—Madame Alvarez (Hermione Gingold) and Gaston Lachaille (Louis Jourdan). [PHOTO M·G·M]

The following morning, bright and early, Gaston is in his uncle's apartment. While Honoré basks in the daily ritual of a shave by his butler Manuel, Gaston paces up and down in a rage of jealousy. During the night, Liane flew the coop with Sandomir. Honoré does his best to persuade his nephew that there is nothing serious in the affair, that this sort of thing happens to everyone; why, it has even happened to Honoré himself. Gaston is inconsolable, though, and in the end his uncle advises him that the only way to set his mind at ease—and to purge his honor—is to go to the country inn where the guilty couple is staying and face them.

Reluctantly Gaston agrees. On the trip out to the country, Honoré is full of gusto, as usual, while Gaston is, also as usual, bored. On arriving at the inn, Gaston marches directly up to Sandomir and Liane, offers the skating instructor ten thousand francs to disappear, and informs Liane that he is through with her for good.

When Sandomir accepts the offer and Liane puts on a suitable show of brokenheartedness, Honoré congratulates Gaston on his superb handling of the affair.

The morning of the next day finds Mme. Alvarez and Aunt Alicia in flurried conversation over the great news that is the talk of Paris. Liane has made an unsuccessful attempt at suicide, the fifth in her career. Gigi's guardians have only contempt for Liane, of course, but they are fascinated by one question: Who will be Liane's successor and get the next crack at the Lachaille millions?

Gaston himself couldn't care less. He is spending the morning at his uncle's apartment, listening indifferently as Honoré exults over the sensation that the breakup and the suicide have caused in Paris society and assures his nephew that now his name as a man of the world is finally made. Gaston only wants to go away and forget the whole thing, but Honoré insists that he owes it to

Cecil Beaton's costume sketch for Gigi.

After dinner, he and Gigi continue their afternoon card game, with Gaston half ironically offering to take Gigi and her grandmother to Trouville for the weekend if he loses. When he really does lose, he is so charmed and comforted by the warm atmosphere of the house and the sheer fun of the day that he decides to make good on his bet. Grandmama is not certain at first whether she ought to accept, but in the end she is persuaded, and Gigi bubbles over with excitement at the prospect in the song "The Night They Invented Champagne" (see p. 186).

As it turns out, Honoré is spending the same weekend at Trouville, pursuing a girl called Simone, who, he knows, has grown tired of her current protector, Prince Berensky. At first, he is delighted to find Gaston and Gigi there too, but his enthusiasm abates a little when he learns that Grandmama has come along with them. For, it develops, Mme. Alvarez was one of Honoré's longest-lived attachments some decades earlier and, though they have not seen one another for years, neither of them ever quite got over the affair.

Time after time, as the weekend proceeds, Honoré is on the point of drawing Simone away from Berensky —on the beach, in the casino, at the tennis courts—when his gaze falls on Grandmama and he melts—long enough, anyway, to lose the golden opportunity. Finally he gives in to the temptation to speak to his old love, and they fall into warm, tender, though slightly vague, reminiscence in the duet "I Remember It Well" (see p. 189).

Meanwhile, the relationship between Gaston and Gigi is visibly ripening as they swim and dance and play tennis together against the background of the luxurious resort. Back in Paris, Aunt Alicia has got wind of what is going on, and as soon as Grandmama returns she is summoned for a conference.

What, Aunt Alicia wonders, are the chances of turning Gaston's interest in Gigi as an innocent companion into something more serious and profitable? Though Grandmama objects that Gigi is still far too young to start on her worldly career, Aunt Alicia insists that the opportunity is too perfect to let pass by.

Now the lessons really begin in earnest. Gigi's every free moment is given to them: spending hours learning how to pour coffee and an afternoon on how to enter a door; growing tipsy over her wine-tasting assignment and ill at her cigarette-smoking session; being taught

the public to play his new role, put on a show, appear everywhere, dazzle Paris.

Once more, Gaston is swayed by his uncle's advice, and he sets himself to the task, though everything about it bores him beyond words. He dines out; he hires restaurants and theaters for his parties; he fetes the most beautiful women in Paris; he gives away fabulous jewelry—in short, he puts on the most lavish display the city has ever seen.

All the while, Gigi is following his performance with avid interest, though naturally at a distance. In fact, she is discussing it with Grandmama one afternoon when Gaston himself arrives, fleeing his own publicity, looking for nothing more than a quiet family day with the Alvarezes, helping Grandmama string beans, eating her simple cooking, playing cards with Gigi. Indeed, the afternoon passes so delightfully that he ends by neglecting to go to a party he is putting on that evening.

Costume sketches by Cecil Beaton.

how to select cigars and being fitted out with a new, mature wardrobe.

And then one afternoon, on coming home from school, she finds Gaston waiting for her with a box of caramels, looking forward to one of their familiar, relaxed afternoons. On an impulse Gigi rushes from the room and returns again a moment later, modeling one of her new, very extreme gowns. Gaston is appalled and Gigi is insulted. They spat and Gaston leaves the house, furious.

A few minutes later he returns, apologetic and eager to make up for his impoliteness by taking Gigi out to tea. Grandmama absolutely refuses to allow it. Sending Gigi out of the room, she explains to Gaston that the situation has changed, that her grandchild is growing into a young woman, that if she were to be seen out with him, her reputation would be compromised. From now on, Grandmama insists, he may not expect to treat her in the offhand fashion he has grown used to.

Upset and confused, Gaston leaves the house to walk the streets of the city. All his ideas about Gigi are at sixes and sevens. Is she a girl or a woman? What does he really feel for her? His long doubts and his final perception that he really does care for her in an adult way crystallize in the sung soliloquy "Gigi" (see p. 194). His mind made up, he rushes back to Mme. Alvarez to announce that he has a business proposition to make.

The next day, Grandmama and Aunt Alicia meet to discuss the terms Gaston has offered. He has promised to make Gigi the best-cared-for and most independent mistress in Paris. Though Aunt Alicia advises caution in the final bargaining, both women are really delighted and can see no reason why a contract should not be signed directly.

But they reckon without Gigi's willfulness. When Gaston comes to confirm the offer to her, he finds her nervous and preoccupied. She says that she understands the proposal and all it implies but that she intends to refuse it. Some of her reasons are childish, but there is much good sense in what she says. She does not covet the dreary ritual of *demimondain* society, and she fears that accepting Gaston's proposal would mean an end to the "little life" she has grown used to with Gaston, with all its gaiety and simplicity. In short, she prefers to go on just as she is.

Now Gaston is really horrified, and he goes off to seek advice from Honoré, who characteristically responds that Gigi is simply out for better terms and that she will come crawling in a day or two. He suggests that Gaston take out a redhead that evening and forget the whole business. After the young man has gone off, his uncle comments on the affair in the song, "I'm Glad I'm Not Young Anymore" (see p. 200).

Meanwhile, a crucial conference is being held between Grandmama and Aunt Alicia, who are as horrified by Gigi's behavior as Gaston is. They are cooking up a scheme to change her mind when Gaston suddenly arrives at the apartment, summoned by a note from Gigi. When she is called from her room, she surprises everyone by announcing that she has decided to accept the offer after all. Overjoyed, Gaston invites her to dine at Maxim's that night to celebrate her decision.

Several hours later Gigi is dressing for the evening, which she realizes will be among the most important of her life. Before her mirror, she sings "Say a Prayer for Me Tonight" (see p. 204). Gaston, meanwhile, is picking out the most expensive diamond bracelet to be found in Paris.

When they arrive together at the restaurant, they

Photographic study by Cecil Beaton of Leslie Caron as Gigi.

make an even more brilliant couple than Gaston and Liane did—and they attract even more attention. Everything is set for Gigi's debut to be either the most spectacular of the century or the greatest flop. And it soon becomes apparent that Gigi has learned every one of Aunt Alicia's lessons by heart and has, in fact, become an expert in all the worldly arts. But that is just the trouble. Gigi outdoes herself selecting cigars with an expert's eye, showing off her expensive jewelry, and gossiping about the other celebrities; in fact, she does it to the point where Gaston can no longer stand it.

She adds a little extra flourish to each gesture, and it is obvious that she is irritating Gaston. But slowly he comes to see the point, and in the end he is quite beyond himself. Bewildered and angry at the performance Gigi has put on—parroting all Liane's dreary affectations and even topping them—Gaston hustles her out of the restaurant and home. As he deposits her on Grandmama's doorstep, it seems that the whole deal must be off.

Once more, Gaston begins to walk off his emotions in the streets of Paris, until suddenly, in a flash, everything becomes quite clear to him. He dashes back to the Alvarez apartment—to offer Gigi a proposal of marriage, which she readily accepts.

The film closes back in the Bois de Boulogne, where it began, with Honoré still at his accustomed spot, still musing over the virtues of little girls and appraising the passing throng, among whom are Gigi and Gaston, the happiest and handsomest married couple of the lot.

Driving in the Bois de Boulogne. Sketch by Cecil Beaton.

THE FIRST LERNER-LOEWE MUSICAL
SINCE "MY FAIR LADY"

M-G-M Presents AN ARTHUR FREED PRODUCTION Starring
LESLIE CARON · MAURICE CHEVALIER · LOUIS JOURDAN
HERMIONE GINGOLD · EVA GABOR · JACQUES BERGERAC · ISABEL JEANS
Screen Play and Lyrics by ALAN JAY LERNER · Music by FREDERICK LOEWE · Based on the Novel by COLETTE
Costumes, Scenery & Production Design by CECIL BEATON · In CinemaScope And METROCOLOR · Directed by VINCENTE MINNELLI

Copyright © 1958 Loew's Incorporated
Country of Origin U. S. A.

Property of National Screen Service Corp. Licensed for display only in connection with
the exhibition of this picture at your theatre. Must be returned immediately thereafter.

58★138

Thank Heaven for Little Girls

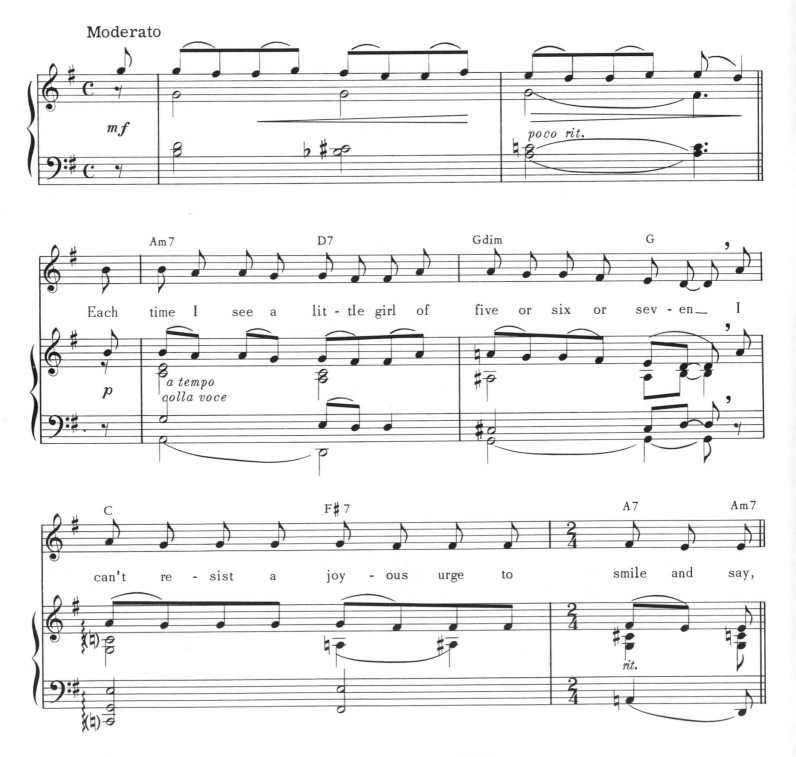

Copyright © 1957 (unpub.) & 1958 by Mara-Lane Music Corporation, New York, N.Y.

Leisurely

Thank hea - ven_____ for lit - tle girls!_____ For

lit - tle girls get big - ger ev - 'ry day_____ Thank

hea - ven_____ for lit - tle girls!_____ They

grow up in the most de - light - ful way._____ Those

Waltz at Maxim's

[SHE IS NOT THINKING OF ME]

Tempo di Valse

She's so gay to-night__ She's like spring to-night__ She's a rol-lick-ing, frol-ick-ing thing to-night__ So dis-arm-ing__ Soft and charm-ing__ She is not think-ing of

Copyright © 1957 (unpub.) & 1958 by Mara-Lane Music Corporation, New York, N.Y.

The Night They Invented Champagne

The night they in-vent-ed cham-pagne,_____ It's plain as it can be They thought of you and me! The

Copyright © 1957 (unpub.) & 1958 by Mara-Lane Music Corporation, New York, N.Y.

I Remember It Well

Copyright © 1957 (unpub.) & 1958 by Mara-Lane Music Corporation, New York, N.Y.

Gigi

Copyright © 1957 (unpub.) & 1958 by Mara-Lane Music Corporation, New York, N.Y.

mir - a - cle has made you the way you are?

Gi - gi, am I a fool with - out a mind or have I

mere - ly been too blind to re - a - lize? Oh, Gi - gi,
Why you've been

grow - ing up be - fore my eyes!

I'm Glad
I'm Not Young Anymore

Copyright © 1957 (unpub.) & 1958 by Mara-Lane Music Corporation, New York, N.Y.

Say a Prayer for Me Tonight

Moderate waltz tempo

Slowly, with feeling

Say   a   prayer   for   me   to - night._____   I'll   need

ev - 'ry   prayer_____   that   you   can   spare   to   get   me   by._____

Copyright © 1957 (unpub.) & 1958 by Mara-Lane Music Corporation, New York, N.Y.

parte. Oh, say a prayer for me this ev' - ning

Bow your head and please stay on your knees to-

poco rall.

1 night.

2 night.

a tempo

a tempo

dolce

rall.

pp

CAMELOT

OPENED DECEMBER 3, 1960, AT THE MAJESTIC THEATRE

Book and Lyrics by ALAN JAY LERNER ❦ *Music by* FREDERICK LOEWE

PRODUCED BY THE MESSRS. LERNER · LOEWE · HART
PRODUCTION STAGED BY MOSS HART
CHOREOGRAPHY AND MUSICAL NUMBERS BY HANYA HOLM
SCENIC PRODUCTION BY OLIVER SMITH
COSTUMES DESIGNED BY ADRIAN AND TONY DUQUETTE
LIGHTING BY FEDER
MUSICAL DIRECTOR: FRANZ ALLERS
ORCHESTRATIONS BY ROBERT RUSSELL BENNETT AND PHILIP J. LANG
DANCE AND CHORAL ARRANGEMENTS BY TRUDE RITTMAN
HAIR STYLES BY ERNEST ADLER
BASED ON *The Once and Future King* BY T. H. WHITE

ORIGINAL CAST
[IN ORDER OF APPEARANCE]

SIR DINADAN	JOHN CULLUM
SIR LIONEL	BRUCE YARNELL
MERLYN	DAVID HURST
ARTHUR	RICHARD BURTON
GUENEVERE	JULIE ANDREWS
NIMUE	MARJORIE SMITH
A PAGE	LELAND MAYFORTH
LANCELOT	ROBERT GOULET
DAP	MICHAEL CLARKE-LAURENCE
PELLINORE	ROBERT COOTE
CLARIUS	RICHARD KUCH
LADY ANNE	CHRISTINA GILLESPIE
A LADY	LEESA TROY
SIR SAGRAMORE	JAMES GANNON
A PAGE	PETER DE VISE
HERALD	JOHN STARKWEATHER
LADY CATHERINE	VIRGINIA ALLEN
MORDRED	RODDY McDOWALL
SIR OZANNA	MICHAEL KERMOYAN
SIR GWILLIAM	JACK DABDOUB
MORGAN LE FEY	M'EL DOWD
TOM	ROBIN STEWART

CAMELOT

CAMELOT MAY WELL HAVE BEEN THE MOST eagerly awaited new production in the history of the theater. It was to be the first Lerner and Loewe Broadway opening after *My Fair Lady*; it had a record budget and an advance sale of more than $2,000,000; the press coverage it received on the road, and even before, was the most exhaustive ever. To add to the suspense, the whole production seemed at the start to be clouded over with bad fortune. Lerner was ill; the original costume designer died; the director, Moss Hart, suffered a heart attack on the road; and the second act had to be rewritten over and over again, down to the week before the opening.

But one dark cloud outglowered all the others. The public—and particularly the theatrical profession— seemed intent on judging the new show by the practically impossible standards of *My Fair Lady*. In the press, in Shubert Alley, throughout the country, it was confidently predicted that *Camelot* could not possibly live up to the example of its distinguished predecessor. In fact, in many minds, one felt, there lurked the sneaking hope that it should not either.

Of all the people concerned, the two who seemed least disturbed by the apparently overwhelming odds were the authors themselves. Shortly after the opening of *My Fair Lady*, they had already begun casting about for a new, even more ambitious subject to tackle. Lerner had found it two years later, when he read the American edition of T. H. White's retelling of the Arthurian legend, *The Once and Future King*. He went through the long book at a gallop, convinced from the first pages that he had discovered exactly what he wanted. He got directly in touch with Loewe, who shared his enthusiasm for the project and agreed to compose the music for it.

The artistic problems were, if anything, still more imposing. White's book had appeared originally in three good-sized volumes. Taken together, they formed a huge, sprawling saga, covering the life of King Arthur from boyhood through youth and young manhood to maturity and death. It contained literally scores of strongly dramatic episodes, dozens of characters, and a web of complicated themes, ranging from statecraft and courtly love to witchcraft and falconry. At the center of the tapestry stood a character of very nearly incredible remoteness and complexity whose motivations and behavior had been probed by hundreds of different authors—and never quite resolved. The most celebrated act was both mysterious and, one would have imagined, dramatically unsuitable: his stubbornly maintained permissiveness toward his wife's adultery.

To help him in the Herculean task of concision, Lerner turned to the older accounts of the legend in Malory and Tennyson. In the end, he found that his own instinct, combined with White's book, was the surest guide. He determined that the play should concentrate on the relationship between Arthur, Guenevere, and Lancelot. More specifically, he decided that Arthur's moral predicament, rather than the love affair itself, should hold the center of the stage.

As with *My Fair Lady,* it became clear that the central role had to be assigned to a dramatic actor of considerable stature. Richard Burton agreed to play the part of Arthur, and he turned out to be, as even the severest critics conceded, the show's strongest asset. But he brought with him, as Harrison had in the previous show, one liability in the lack of a conventional, trained "singing" voice. His songs had to be carefully tailored to suit his particular musical personality.

The old problem of the relationship between song and story, the principle that each song should be strictly motivated by character, came up again, and in even more critical form than in all the earlier shows. The pomp and glory of the court setting—though in one way conferring obvious advantages—formed, in another, an obstacle in that elaborate care had to be taken to insure that the central characters would not be lost in the swirling panoply. The danger was most acute in the rush of events that formed the last half of the second act. Here and elsewhere in the play, a severe stylization of both action and music was imposed to maintain the coherence of the narrative.

The task that lay closest to Lerner's heart was perhaps the most difficult of all. White's notion of the political significance of the Round Table was, Lerner felt, of paramount importance. Among other things, it went a long way toward explaining Arthur's nearly saintlike tolerance of his wife's infidelity. But the concept that Camelot represented a kind of idealization of civilized society, in which order and peace imposed a sometimes cruel discipline on everyone, and most of all on the king was as intricate as it was powerful.

Lerner would make no compromises on this central theme. He built toward it through the whole first act. It was presented with an absolute forthrightness by the king himself at the first-act curtain. Some critics suggested that now at last Lerner and Loewe had stretched the popular musical theater beyond its capacity and strayed into an area where only straight drama or opera could reasonably be expected to serve their ends.

It is a measure of the radical change that had come over the American musical stage in the last decade that criticism along these lines was as scattered as it was. A majority of the critics applauded the work. There was nothing but praise for Richard Burton's authoritative performance; and the rich—sometimes gay, sometimes austere—settings by Oliver Smith and costumes by Adrian and Tony Duquette were universally hailed.

The inevitable objection was raised that *Camelot* had not lived up to the standard of *My Fair Lady*. But it was not long before a wave of common-sense reaction to this view set in. After all, the earlier show was something like perfection in its way: a standard, it was pointed out, that even Lerner and Loewe need not be expected to meet.

Moreover, the scale and style of *Camelot* were more ambitious than those of its predecessor. *Camelot* had set out to capture the essence of one of the fundamental myths of Western civilization. The consensus of the capacity audiences who have crowded to see it is that it roundly achieved its aim.

It would be extreme to suggest that Lerner and Loewe have effected a single-handed revolution in the American musical theater. It is unarguable, though, that they have been, along with Rodgers and Hammerstein, the pioneers in a deep and probably permanent process of evolution: away from review and everything it stands for and toward maturity and complexity of plot; the organic integration of song, dance, and story; the interdependence of song with character; and the willingness to deal with material conventionally regarded as too intellectual or unromantic for treatment on the popular musical stage.

KING ARTHUR is first seen on his wedding day. Though the procession of his betrothed, the princess

Al Hirschfeld's depiction of Richard Burton as Arthur, Julie Andrews as
Guenevere, Robert Goulet as Lancelot, and Roddy McDowall as Mordred.

Guenevere, has just been sighted from the heights of
Camelot, the young king is far from prepared to give
her the state reception that has been scheduled. In fact,
he is at the moment hiding in a treetop on a hill near
the castle, frightened out of his wits. His old tutor
Merlyn the Magician is trying to jolly him into behav-
ing like a monarch by recalling the king's responsibility
to his people, by stressing the charms of the prospective
bride, by chiding and cajoling—but all to no avail. The
king is dead scared and ready to admit it, as he does
quite frankly in the song "I Wonder What the King Is
Doing Tonight?" (see p. 218).

Just as this confession ends, a lovely young woman
wanders onstage, evidently lost. It is Guenevere, who,
equally frightened by all the pomp and circumstance,
has also fled the reception. Thinking herself alone, she
sings a brief prayer to her patron saint Genevieve and
then, in a longer-sung soliloquy, asks, "Where Are the
Simple Joys of Maidenhood?"

Suddenly the bough on which Arthur is perched

snaps, and he tumbles to the ground at Guenevere's side. Unaware of who he is, the princess is terrified and antagonistic. Arthur, on the other hand, is stunned by Guenevere's extraordinary charm and beauty.

The king finds himself in the odd position—for a king —of having to woo his bride, but it is a task which he proves capable of performing royally as he gradually sets the princess's mind at ease and begins to win her over to the (to her) distasteful idea of living in Camelot. He even goes so far as to sing her a sales talk on the place, the title song, "Camelot" (see p. 225). In the course of his talk with Guenevere, he describes his boyhood and education under Merlyn's guidance, and in the end he reveals his identity. By this time he has got around to the point of admitting that the prospect of *not* marrying now seems more awful than the reverse.

In the following scene, later that day, a momentous event in Merlyn's life takes place. Since he can see forward into the future, he has long known that he would one day be called away from the world of men by the nymph Nimue and that he would be obliged to fade away into the world of magic. His only worry has been that Arthur should be safely settled before he goes. Now that Arthur has married Guenevere, the long-awaited call finally comes; the voice of Nimue is heard singing the siren song "Follow Me" (see p. 230), and Merlyn follows it to his destiny, remembering only when it is too late that he has neglected to warn the king of . . . a number of things.

The next scene occurs five years later in the royal apartments at Camelot, where Arthur and Guenevere are deep in serious conversation. Their marriage and the nation have prospered, but Arthur has become increasingly preoccupied with the barbarous violence of the times and with the fact that all his power and the skills of his knights are directed toward war, killing, and the piling up of might. Now an idea he has been mulling over for a long time begins to take shape. He decides to form a new order of chivalry—the Round Table, in which might will be used only in the service of right and in which the tasks of the knights will be to administer established laws, to protect the weak, and to maintain justice. Guenevere approves the idea enthusiastically, and the proclamation goes out that very day.

One of the first knights to be attracted by the new order is the young, dashing, almost incredibly virtuous Frenchman, Lancelot du Lac, who is soon on his way to England, overflowing with enthusiasm and confidence, impatient to get on with the business of the Round Table.

In the woods just outside Camelot, he encounters a suspicious-seeming knight, whom he swiftly unhorses only to discover—to his intense embarrassment—that the knight is Arthur himself. When the king revives and meets his assailant, he greets him warmly and welcomes him into the company of the Round Table. But Lancelot demurs; he must first, he insists, perform some deed of valor to prove his worthiness. Arthur proves an acute disappointment to the young knight when he informs him that there are, in fact, no pressing acts of knight-errantry on the agenda just at the moment. Instead, the court is on its way to join the queen, who is a-Maying in the woods nearby, and Arthur invites Lancelot to come along.

The scene shifts to Guenevere and her party, for all of whom Guenevere sets the tone with the gay, colorful, slightly bawdy song "The Lusty Month of May" (see p. 233). In a moment or two, the party is interrupted by the appearance of the eccentric, clanking figure of one King Pellinore, who, despite appearances, turns out to have been a boon companion of the young King Arthur when he was nothing more than an obscure squire named Wart. The friendship has lapsed over the last years, as King Pelly has been preoccupied with his endless quest for the fabulous Questing Beast, curse of the Pellinores. Thoroughly enchanted by the old character, Guenevere invites him to give up the quest for a time and come to stay at Camelot.

Immediately after, Arthur enters with Lancelot, whom he introduces to the queen. Moments later, the young knight is off on one of his obsessional monologues about knighthood and purity, clearly irritating Guenevere but also, against her will, impressing her. The subject of Lancelot's deed of valor comes up again, and Arthur suggests a tournament, an offer that Lancelot accepts, on condition that he be matched against not one champion but three. Sir Lionel, Sir Sagramore, and Sir Dinadan, the three champion jousters of the court, take up the challenge.

In the following scene, Arthur, Lancelot, and Pelly are on the castle terrace, with the two kings playing backgammon while Lancelot, with overweening conceit and high-mindedness, rereads a proclamation he has prepared on the training of knights-errant. Arthur and Pelly are able to take his somewhat annoying manner in stride, but in a moment the queen enters, and it is

Into "The Lusty Month of May" scene, Sir Lancelot introduces a serious note with his idea for training knights of the Round Table. [PHOTO FRIEDMAN–ABELES]

clear as day that the French knight has already driven her to the limit of her patience. Lancelot exits abruptly, after which Arthur and Guenevere fall into conversation about the tournament that is scheduled for the following day. It emerges that Guenevere has authorized each of the knights opposing Lancelot to wear her special colors. Arthur is scandalized at this display of favoritism and pleads with Guenevere to retract, but she refuses. Flabbergasted, Arthur confesses his entire inability to understand or deal with the gentle sex in the sung soliloquy "How to Handle a Woman" (see p. 236).

The tournament opens the next day in a splendor of fanfares and elegance. Everyone is convinced that Lancelot will be defeated by his English opponents, but, instead, he unseats first Sir Dinadan and then Sir Sagramore with consummate facility. In the last and crucial joust, he not only unhorses Sir Lionel but kills him. In the midst of the uproar of shock, consternation, and anger that follows, Lancelot approaches the inert form of the fallen knight, takes his limp hand, and—by an undoubted miracle—revives him.

In the castle that evening, there is a hullabaloo of general excitement and enthusiasm surrounding Lancelot. Only Arthur and Guenevere seem subdued and preoccupied as they go about preparing for Lancelot's triumphal investment into the order. When Arthur leaves the room for a moment, the queen reveals in a soliloquy that the young French knight no longer arouses her antagonism but, quite to the contrary, so strongly attracts her as to make her life miserable. Her realization that she will somehow have to get away from him if she is to avoid the trap of illicit love is expressed in the song "Before I Gaze at You Again" (see p. 239).

Lancelot enters, suddenly breaking into Guenevere's reverie. Irresistibly impelled, he confesses that he has fallen in love with her, and she, equally against her will, assures him that she has loved him from the day they met. A moment later, Arthur returns, and though it is obvious that he senses the meaning of the situation, all three do their best to gloss it over.

Together they proceed to the Grand Hall of the castle, where Lancelot's investiture is to take place. It is an extraordinarily moving occasion, simple and immensely dignified. When it is accomplished, the court retires, leaving Arthur alone and obliged to face up to the terrible problem posed by Lancelot and the queen. Were he but a man among other men, he would have no difficulty making his decision. But he is a king as well as a man, and he is forced to set the example of civilized conduct. After long, heavy consideration, he realizes that he must restrain his jealousy—for the sake of court and country.

The second act takes place several years later, and it is clear that Arthur has managed to maintain his heartbreaking resolve. Lancelot and Guenevere are found seated on the castle terrace, the knight, in the tradition of courtly love, serenading his beloved with a song of his own composition, "If Ever I Would Leave You" (see p. 242). In the conversation that follows, Lancelot and Guenevere reassure one another that Arthur knows nothing of their long-standing relationship. Shortly, Guenevere is called for by her ladies-in-waiting, and Lancelot follows her offstage.

A young Scotsman enters, a dark, cruel, devious-looking figure. The king enters a moment later, encounters the young man, and falls into a conversation with him, during the course of which the youth announces, with a sneering impertinence, that he is Mordred, son of Morgause. Arthur is stunned by this news, as it means that the repulsive young man must be his own son. When the king was a young man himself, the wicked Morgause had bewitched him for one night and seduced him in order to get a son by him. Now, of course, Arthur has no choice but to keep Mordred on at Camelot, but he warns him nevertheless that he will be sent away at the first sign of active maliciousness.

In the next scene, a month later, Arthur and Guenevere are seated together on the castle terrace. As usual, the king is up to his neck in the day-to-day problems of state, but these have paled to insignificance beside the menace into which Mordred's presence has developed. Just as Arthur and Guenevere are discussing the problem of what to do with the boy, Pelly comes in with fresh evidence that Mordred is doing everything in his power to undermine the king's authority, to ridicule

the court, and to cause strife and dissension. Overcome by the situation, the king and queen set themselves to wondering "What Do Simple Folk Do?" (see p. 246) when things get to be too much for them, but the answers they arrive at are no help at all.

Meanwhile, Mordred is prowling about the forest near Camelot in search of his aunt, the wicked fairy Morgan Le Fey, who reigns over a mysterious court in the depths of the forest that is invisible to human eyes. Knowing that his aunt is prey to an irresistible sweet tooth, Mordred wanders about the woods calling out that he will give her a bag of cherry creams if she will only appear. In the end, the fairy queen gives in to temptation and her whole sinister establishment shudders into visibility.

But Mordred is prepared to cheat even his own aunt. He will not hand over the sweets until Morgan agrees to do him a small favor: to build a wall of invisible bricks around King Arthur while he is hunting in the forest, so as to keep him away from the castle for a while. Morgan resists at first, but Mordred teases her mercilessly with promises of marzipan and fudge till finally she gives in.

Later that day, Arthur and Pelly arrive in the forest. When Arthur wanders off by himself for a moment, Morgan's minions duly construct the magic barrier around him, and Mordred is free to pursue his nasty schemes at leisure.

That evening, the wicked prince assembles five strong, traitorous knights about him in a corridor of the castle and settles down to await events. Just as he

Court costume design by Adrian.

Oliver Smith's design for the Queen's bedchamber in Act II.

Mordred (Roddy McDowall) and his followers break in on Guenevere (Julie Andrews) and Lancelot (Robert Goulet). [PHOTO FRIEDMAN–ABELES]

had expected, Lancelot is unable to resist the temptation offered by Arthur's absence and, soon after Guenevere retires, slips into her bedchamber. There she sings to him a final love song, "I Loved You Once in Silence" (see p. 251). For the first time in their long years of love, he pleads with Guenevere to come away with him to France. She refuses, of course, but it is at this point that Mordred and his men burst into the room. The reputations of both the lovers are utterly compromised. Though the men do their best to capture Lancelot, he fights his way out of the room and escapes from the castle.

There follows a kind of musical montage of the events of the next weeks. Lancelot has returned to his own castle in France and Arthur has been unable to prevent Guenevere's being tried for adultery by the court at Camelot. She has been found guilty and sentenced to die at the stake. Now torn between saving Guenevere's life—and so shattering the legal system he has spent his life building up—and allowing her to die horribly under his eyes, Arthur has lost all his capacity for action.

In the last hour before the sentence is scheduled to be executed, Arthur, still undecided, his will all but vanished, is pacing back and forth on a hill above Camelot. Suddenly, at the very last moment, there is the sound of a horn in the south and the army of Lancelot appears riding to the rescue. There is a bloody, terrible battle between the French forces and the men of Camelot, and though, in the end, Guenevere is saved, the loss of life is heavy and the authority of the Round Table is severely lessened.

War is once again loose in the world, and Arthur is left with no choice but to carry the battle to Lancelot at Joyous Gard. The final scene occurs at dawn, on the battlefield before Lancelot's castle, where the three principals meet one final time before the battle is engaged. To his great joy, Arthur learns that Guenevere has come through her ordeal unhurt, but for him, as for her and Lancelot as well, the reunion is overshadowed by the realization that the ideals of the Round Table have been destroyed for the present generation and that the bloody specter of war has risen once again. Guenevere offers to solve the problem by returning to Camelot to be executed, but Arthur, of course, cannot accept this sacrifice. The three friends part on a somber note, each man going off to his camp of war and Guenevere going to the convent where she plans to spend the rest of her days.

Just as the last preparations for the battle are completed, Arthur encounters a young English boy, one Tom of Warwick, who has stowed away on the English ship and come to fight for his hero Arthur. In him, the king recognizes the image of himself as the young squire Wart, full of ideals and dawning manliness, and he is touched almost to tears. Then, suddenly, he has an inspiration.

He orders the boy not to fight in the coming battle but, instead, to return directly to England, where his mission will be to tell the story of Camelot to anyone who will listen, to expound the ideals of the Round Table, and to preserve the memory of the great experiment, so that it may be available to a later age. When the boy willingly, even eagerly, agrees, Arthur is able to go off to face his destiny with a lighter heart.

Julie Andrews as Queen Guenevere leads the ensemble in "The Lusty Month of May." [PHOTO FRIEDMAN–ABELES]

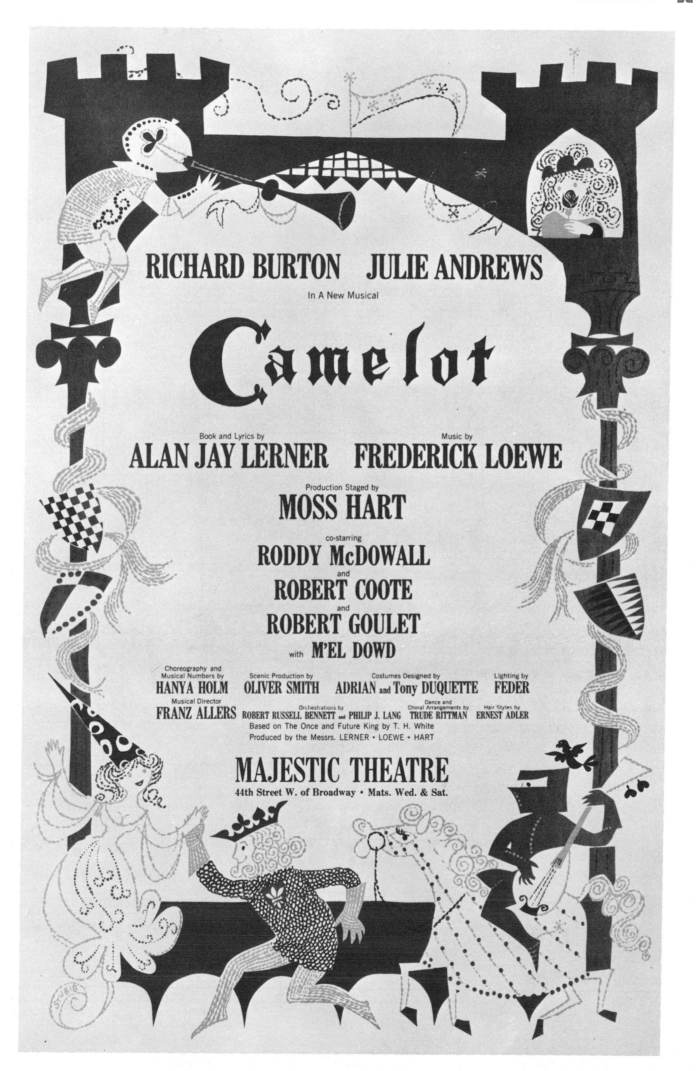

i wonder what the king is doing tonight?

Copyright © 1960 (unpub.) & 1962 by Alan Jay Lerner and Frederick Loewe
Chappell & Co., Inc., New York, N.Y., Publisher and Owner of allied rights with Alfred Productions, Inc.

CAMELOT

Copyright © 1960 by Alan Jay Lerner and Frederick Loewe.
Chappell & Co., Inc., New York, N.Y., Publisher and Owner of allied rights with Alfred Productions, Inc.

FOLLOW ME

Copyright © 1960 by Alan Jay Lerner and Frederick Loewe
Chappell & Co., Inc., New York, N.Y., Publisher and Owner of allied rights with Alfred Productions, Inc.

Tempo I°

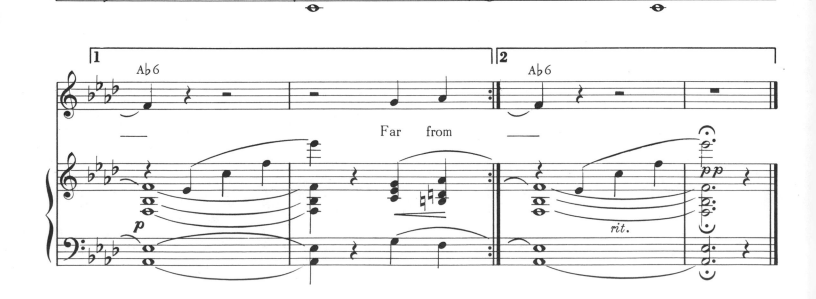

The Lusty Month of May

Allegro giocoso

Copyright © 1960 (unpub.) & 1961 by Alan Jay Lerner and Frederick Loewe
Chappell & Co., Inc., New York, N.Y., Publisher and Owner of allied rights with Alfred Productions, Inc.

how to handle a woman

Copyright © 1960 by Alan Jay Lerner and Frederick Loewe
Chappell & Co., Inc., New York, N.Y., Publisher and Owner of allied rights with Alfred Productions, Inc.

BEFORE I GAZE AT YOU AGAIN

Moderato

Be-fore I gaze at you a-gain I'll need a time for tears. Be-fore I gaze at you a-gain Let hours turn to years. I have so much for-get-ting to do Be-

Copyright © 1960 (unpub.) & 1962 by Alan Jay Lerner and Frederick Loewe
Chappell & Co., Inc., New York, N.Y., Publisher and Owner of allied rights with Alfred Productions, Inc.

if ever i would leave you

Copyright © 1960 by Alan Jay Lerner and Frederick Loewe.
Chappell & Co., Inc., New York, N.Y., Publisher and Owner of allied rights with Alfred Productions, Inc.

WHAT DO SIMPLE FOLK DO?

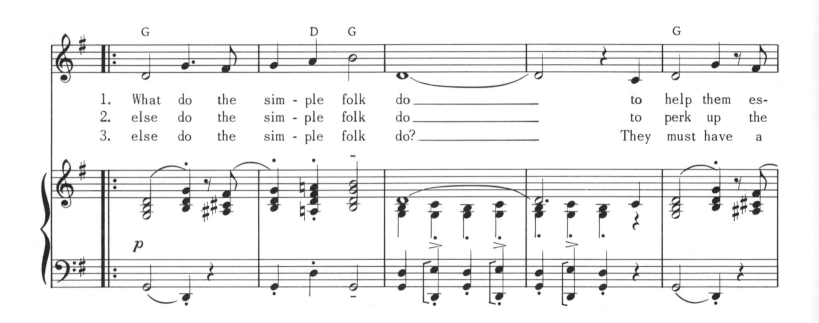

1. What do the sim-ple folk do _____ to help them es-
2. else do the sim-ple folk do _____ to perk up the
3. else do the sim-ple folk do? _____ They must have a

cape when they're blue? _____ The shep-herd who is ail-ing, The
heart and get through? _____ The wee folk and the grown folk, who
sys-tem or two. _____ They ob-vious-ly out-shine us at

Copyright © 1960 (unpub.) & 1961 by Alan Jay Lerner and Frederick Loewe
Chappell & Co., Inc., New York, N.Y., Publisher and Owner of allied rights with Alfred Productions, Inc.

i Loved you once in silence

Copyright © 1960 by Alan Jay Lerner and Frederick Loewe
Chappell & Co., Inc., New York, N.Y., Publisher and Owner of allied rights with Alfred Productions, Inc.

Index of Song and Show Titles

Song titles in roman, show and movie titles in italics.